Electric
Full Stops

Electric Full Stops

Award-winning entries
from the 1995
W H Smith
Young Writers' Competition

MACMILLAN
CHILDREN'S BOOKS

First published 1996 by Macmillan Children's Books
a division of Macmillan Publishers Limited
25 Eccleston Place, London SW1W 9NF
and Basingstoke

Associated companies throughout the world

ISBN 0 333 65489 7

1 3 5 7 9 8 6 4 2

A CIP catalogue record for this book is available from
the British Library

Phototypeset by Intype London Ltd
Printed by Mackays of Chatham PLC, Kent

Contents

INTRODUCTION

At the Prizewinners' Party last summer, I listened to much of the work published in this book when it was performed by the actors Maureen Beattie and Richard Hope. I am daunted when I think that this introduction will precede it. The oldest writer in this book will be me; the next oldest will be one third my age. I cannot hope to be as surprising, forthright, original or thought-provoking as these young writers.

Paradoxically, youth is a positive disqualification from publication for young writers. Publishers argue that writers and their writing need to mature before they are given the chance to be published. They are nervous of young authors – they don't believe that readers will want to read them, or, more importantly, buyers will want to buy their books.

Yet some youthful novelists have prevailed against this prejudice. Nine-year-old Daisy Ashford's *The Young Visiters* has been in print more or less continuously since 1919; Shena Mackay and Guy Burt, both past *Young Writers' Competition* winners, wrote their first published novels when they were seventeen and nineteen respectively. These are notable exceptions, however, to a rule which holds that young writers cannot engage and entertain the reader as completely as adults.

Yet I defy you to read eight-year-old Alexandra Laight's essay on *Love* and not be amazed by the breadth of her observation and by her understanding of human relationships. Her clear-eyed, matter-of-fact approach has much of Daisy Ashford in it, although she was two years younger than Miss Ashford when she wrote her piece. Moreover, at the age of seven she chose to write a piece of discursive prose, a factual analysis, not the more obvious story that one would expect from one so young.

Who could fail to be moved and impressed by Special Award-winner Eva Okwonga's short story *A Letter for Ayatt*? Structurally, linguistically and emotionally – at every level – it is wholly satisfying. The story has moments, such as Okech Samma's letter to his big sister, exiled and alone in the UK, that live with you long after the book is put down. Eva was fifteen when she wrote this.

In the year of the quarter centenary of the W H Smith *Poets in Schools Scheme*, poets are especially important to us. Sarah Stringer gives a perfect example of how young writers are capable of a wide stylistic and emotional range with the two poems which won her a Special Award in 1995. In *Poetic Justice* she sentences her offender to "six months'/heavy labour in the/writers' block of the local/poetentiary", an inspired and exuberant piece of wordplay. In altogether graver mood in *Coaldust* she explores a conflict of opposites in a series of striking images.

This book could not happen, of course, without the faith and energetic support of families and teachers. Throughout the year we receive hundreds of inquiries about the Competition. The many teachers and parents who contact us are unanimous in their belief in the talent of their young writers. That faith is enormously important in the development of any child. To be told when you are struggling with a task that others have complete confidence in your ability to master it, is a powerful incentive to succeed.

Families are central to this confidence-building. They cannot help it – they know their children are unique and wonderful. They know better than anyone the unusual and illuminating things their children have said and done since infancy. They encourage and admire. They lay foundations.

Teachers account for ninety percent of the total entry to the competition. They set up writing workshops, discuss work with individual writers, inspire, chase and cajole. Then they parcel up all the work, sometimes hundreds of entries at a time, and send it in. It is a huge task, undertaken in addition to the teaching, supervision, marking, preparation, testing, record-keeping and counselling which account for just part of a teacher's daily duties.

Why has W H Smith run the *Young Writers' Competition* for nineteen uninterrupted years? It has a lot to do with the way we see ourselves as a leading retailer of books, newspapers, magazines and stationery. The business deals in all the sophisticated means of communication that a cultured society has developed over hundreds of years. It attends to people's desire to know and learn and enjoy life. It responds to people's aspirations for themselves and for their families, to their need for a varied pattern of leisure, to the necessity of keeping in touch with contemporary issues. So it is unsurprising that we have chosen, over 25 years, to support educational projects in our sponsorship programme – the *Poets in Schools Scheme* and the *Young Writers' Competition* are two long-standing examples of this.

The *Young Writers' Competition* allows us to say as publicly as we can that we are on the side of parents who want their children to get the most out of their schooling, on the side of teachers who have the sometimes rewarding and often exhausting task of inspiring and educating young people, and on the side of young people who want to communicate with a wider audience than just their friends, family and teachers. We want to celebrate their achievement and encourage others. Above all, we enjoy sharing the pleasure of running the competition by publishing this book.

Jeremy Hardie
Chairman, W H Smith Group

Advisory panel of judges: Ted Hughes (Chairman), John Agard, Michael Baldwin, Adèle Geras, Janni Howker, Jan Mark and Kit Wright.

Preliminary panel of judges: Lynn Barclay, Richard Brookfield, Charlotte Brook-Smith, Linda Hoare, Anna Hopewell, Barry Maybury, Richard Quarshie, Timothy Rogers, Betty Rosen, Professor Harold Rosen, Sheila Shannon, Tony Weeks-Pearson.

THROUGH THE DOOR TO THE WHOLE WIDE WORLD

Peck Sun Goh (16)

Emily Fleuriot (16)

*The Beginning of a Story . . .

Joanna entered her room in a state of anxiety. She flung her
pile of papers and books on her bed and sat at her desk,
slumped in front of her typewriter. She had just got back
from her publishers and they hadn't liked the idea. She had
wanted to produce an entirely different style book to the
ones she had produced so far in her literary career. It was a
story of love and lust, unfulfilment and unhappiness, Joanna
was actually quite pleased with it, it was a bit of a giggle,
and quite unlike anything else she had ever written. She had
thought of becoming a "Johanna" by adding an H to her
christian name and then maybe even change her surname to
something like "Allured" or "Lehman", anything was more
interesting than her present name. But no, it wasn't the right
kind of style that the public wanted from her. Mr Smiggles,
of Smiggles and Bartley, wanted her usual detective novel,
and had cursed her manuscript as a worthless piece of work
not fit for Smiggles & Bartley and more suited to Mills &
Boon (though of course not in so many words).

Anyway, Joanna still had to meet the deadline in seven
weeks' time, as Mr Bartley was most particular that
creativity, even works of art should be forced, it seemed to
Joanna T. Angel. Pushing against her desk with her feet she
wheeled the four feet across the room to her filing cabinet
on her second-hand office chair, bought from a police station
clearout near her parents' village for about twelve pounds.
Opening the bottom drawer she pulled out an inch-thick wad
of plain paper, a file labelled "ideas" and two pots of correction fluid, plus thinner as at least one bottle was bound to
have lumps in. She wheeled back across to her desk, and

2

carefully arranged her work space. Joanna never usually did this, but she figured that if her creativity was being forced into neatness and was being organised she'd better be. She placed the plain paper to the left of the typewriter and the correction fluid to the right. Then she fumbled around in the top drawer of her desk until she found her favourite pens for working with; these she placed on the right hand side of the typewriter along with a few boiled sweets she found floating around with them. Then she opened the file of ideas and began to work on some of the rough drafts.

Half an hour later Joanna looked up and pushed back the nylon net curtain which separated her, her room and her desk from the world outside. In the rooms opposite were some offices. She could see business men and women in their smart, dark suits trying to win customers over into buying, selling or neither. The stark yellowing lights made an iridescent glow in the small area outside of their windows, in the lengthening shadows of the coming evening. Winter depressed Joanna, there was no doubt, and it was true she had written more in summers and her two bestsellers were her summer novels. The critics seemed to love her books more in the summer, one had even dubbed her the new Agatha Christie which she had been happy about. Joanna leant back over her chair and stretched then slapped her wrists and told herself to get a move on and produce something absolutely wonderful for S&B. She had chosen the lost jewel causing murder and superstition among an Irish aristocratic family. Unfortunately, much to Joanna's false dismay she needed to do much more research before being able to get past the first twenty pages. She decided to leave it for a while and just continued watching her neighbourhood carry out its life. At the corner stood a policeman moving along a homeless couple from a doorway to a shop that had long since closed down. Mrs Pastry was locking up the chemist which she ran with her younger sister Maddy; she put up her umbrella as small drops of rain started to drip, first slow slow slow, then quicker and quicker although it still remained a "dry", unwetting rain that passes over you. Joanna did not see whether Mrs Pastry put the umbrella down when the rain stopped, as she was probably home by then anyway. She watched the red neon light flicker on and off erratically, spelling out "PRESCRIPTIONS", then focused her attention on the off-licence next door. The two shops on either side of it were both closed, and on the side opposite the chemists, three shops in a row were shut. By the furthest of the three shops stood a group of about ten youths. Joanna didn't like the word teenager and never had, not even when she'd been one, but she wasn't exactly ecstatic about "youths" either. At that moment in time she wasn't actually particularly bothered with their names, more their actions.

The group standing in the alley way three shops away from the off-licence were a mixture of both boys and girls. Using her niece, Miranda, who was fourteen, as a standard fourteen year old, Joanna judged them, perhaps wrongly, to be around fifteen. A few, mainly the girls, looked slightly older; the darkness didn't exactly help judgement. Joanna stood up and opened the window quite widely, but allowed the net curtains to fall almost back into place, hooking them back with a rusty nail embedded into the windowsill that she had never got round to pulling out. She then clambered up onto her desk, difficult, especially as she hadn't done it for at least a decade. She knocked off a few pens and pots, and had to move the typewriter but got quite comfortable after a fashion. She knew she was acting like a nosy old moo and was enjoying every minute of it. About three of the group, the ones that Joanna had considered the older looking ones, collected money from everyone else. Their voices were easily audible as the traffic wasn't too busy. They were discussing

4

what should be bought by the boy and two girls, evidently from the off-licence. She felt like a moron. She had done exactly the same thing about fifteen years ago. It seemed to be a choice, or argument, between white wine, gets you drunk quick, cider, gets you drunk quick and no vomiting, or lager, tastes gross but does the job and is cheap. Joanna laughed to herself, it was still the same! She felt like shouting "cider!" but decided not to, in the end that was what they decided to get anyway, with the exception of lager for "Nik". The three walked calmly down the street and through the entrance, and Joanna almost held her breath, she was so intrigued to see whether they got served or not. Maybe she should investigate and write a report on it or not on it she didn't really know, she just watched and waited. In only a few minutes they came back from out of the off-licence, triumphantly carrying large green paper bags, the clinking of bottles ringing from them. At this point Joanna got bored and came away from the window, closing it.

She took the file of ideas, some paper and pen through to her kitchen in case inspiration came to her whilst cooking her dinner, although what storyline she could build using lasagne she had no idea. As she chopped the carrots, tomatoes and mushrooms she was thinking of a story that was what Smiggles wanted without it being boring and exactly the same as her last novels. She needed to change the style in which she wrote in whatever way possible, but sensibly speaking, not too different and out of the ordinary from her usual stuff.

By now Joanna had got on to cutting up the onion. The gases were making her eyes water, rows and rows of tears ran down her cheeks and dropped from her chin; then continued down her neck to be soaked up by the executive striped shirt she'd worn to look as professional and business-like as possible. Truth was she didn't consider herself to be either, and was literally "dressed to impress". She stalled her cutting onions for a second, absentmindedly she dipped her finger into the stew of vegetables which was soon to be the main ingredient of her lasagne and tasted it. She decided it was most definitely too sweet, her mother was right, you couldn't get good tomatoes in England. She reached up to the cupboard above the hob and took down the blue plastic cylinder of table salt, tipped about a teaspoonful into her hand and sprinkled it in a swirl over the stew, and resumed chopping onions. Stupidly, it seemed to her at the time, but on reflection afterwards wasn't, she rubbed an index finger well anointed with onion oil across her eyelid, causing it to sting greatly. She ran half blindly across the hallway to the bathroom. Her eye was stinging so badly that no matter what way she splashed water into her eye it wouldn't get better. It was the kind of annoyance she didn't need after a day of rejections, she was really angry, a completely un-directed anger, with perhaps a hint of sub-consciously directed anger lying close beneath the surface.

Having eased the pain in her eye to a certain extent Joanna walked back to the kitchen again just as the sauce began to bubble over the top of the orange enamel saucepan. She grabbed the handle with both hands and placed it on the wooden chopping board, spilling a small lava flow over the edge, which collected in a small pool at its base.

Joanna let out a loud scream. The tuneless piano tunes that so often floated up through her floor from Gertrude Fluaraide's "parlour" stopped, as Gertrude made sure that no-one was being killed or something. Asserting that no-one was being killed the piano music began floating again, much to Joanna's dismay. She swam her hand around in the greying dirty dish water, searching for the cloth amongst the plates and bowls which had been growing in number since yester-day evening. She triumphantly pulled it out, unravelling it from the prongs of a carving fork, which shouldn't have been there as she never used it to get it dirty enough to wash, squeezed it out and wiped up the mess on the hob then the board, lifting the saucepan and cleaning its base. She pulled out one of the dipped wood chairs and sat on it, slapping the cloth on the table, making a smear of faintly bubbly water. Not hygienic, she knew but couldn't honestly be bothered to get the appointed cloth out.

She sunk her head into the cradle of her arms and had a good solid think. The vegetables began to go cold and the pasta remained unopened in the cupboard by the jelly pack. She was really annoyed and angry and still trying to decide what to write her story on. She thought a bit more, she wasn't really exactly angry, more hurt, and she still didn't want to write the same sort of story as she had done the last four times. She opened the folder again and began to read all the flow charts and roughs she'd written over the past five weeks. The words became indistinct bluish black blots and dashes, okay, so she wasn't exactly concentrating on them and didn't want to. She gave up and just fell into a doze. Just more than half an hour but less than an hour later she awoke as the clock struck seven o'clock. She'd been dreaming about things and things and other things and felt most definitely refreshed. As she opened her eyelids they flickered at the surprise of the bright light overhead. She smiled and her eyes flashed wildly from her reflection looking back at her within the wrought-iron framed mirror across the table. She'd had the most amazing inspiration for her story. She had a feeling about this one, better than her last inspirations, and, if Smiggles OR Bartley didn't like this one then she'd tell them where to go. She'd find a decent publishers which allowed her to be her own writer, her own person.

Joanna threw her folder frisbee style through the upper half of the kitchen window where it hit the steel fire escape with a clang. She walked out of the kitchen resolutely and this time rolled into the chair at her desk rather than slumping. Almost excitedly she fed a piece of paper into the typewriter, she was going to actually write something completely from the top of her head, no doubt it would need serious alterations later. She switched on the typewriter at the mains then switched on the actual machine. It was all ready. She adjusted the margins and began to type. The tape ran out. She'd written two letters and it had run out. The shops were all shut by now, she'd have to keep it in her mind until the morning.

"Damn." Joanna sighed, and fumbled around in her coat for a cigarette.

James Stanton (8)

"Amy in the kitchen at Banks Head"
(Winifred Nicholson 1929)

Amy comes into the kitchen.
She is carrying bread and fish.
She looks at me with her big brown eyes
And smiles across the table.

In front of her are the flowers
She spent the morning arranging,
A selection of reds, yellows and purples
Set in snowy ceramics and glass jugs.

These are engraved with wonderful patterns
Of deer, birds and plough horses,
Whose furrows almost extend
To the blue ripples on the table cloth.

Amy is housemaid at Banks Head.
With her curly ginger hair
And a pinny of blues, pinks and oranges
She smiles across the table.

Nareene Kaloyan (15)

Daniel Murray (10)

*Sloane Square

Through the school's corridor
   with pictures of Field Day
followed by the smells of
   teachers' cooking, we go
through the door to
   the Whole Wide World

The marble floor, the
   iron railings, the
rough bricks, the
   scream of glee from
children, the big school
   buses and the signs

Through the car-mending building
   with broken and smashed cars,
past Peter Jones and his
   necklace of roads, we enter
the long streets

Taxis charge, cars rush,
   buses march, vans walk by,
"Say It With Flowers" is on
   the island next to
the useful Smiths,
   Peter Jones sells hats,
chairs, tables, toys and gear

Across the road; when
    the man's red with
anger, he stops you but
    when he's green with
joy he lets you go

The ice-cold water
    in the middle of
the island; the water stings
    your hand like an angry
wasp. Pigeons have a refreshing
    bath while trees hover you

Like skinny trees the
    lampposts stand.
The great trees are
    rough. The Great
World War statue guards
    while pigeons drop bombs
like Hitler's deadly
    Stuka dive bombers

The air smells of
    fumes and dirt,
Old fogies sit down
    on the benches,
gargoyles glare at you

Health shops stand in
   the polluted London air as
well as clothes and shoes
   and yummy food shops

In the army base, the Duke
   of York's boys run
while spies come in
   but not out.

She

Sensation embraced her, encouraging her to touch and feel and explore. To learn through the gentleness of her finger-tips and the softness of her skin, tingling at the anticipation of contact. Trembling with excitement she began to move through the damp, dewy grass that clung to her ankles and licked her legs as its regal poise was disturbed by her vibrant body. She felt the cold, crumbly earth nestle itself between the fingers of her feet each time her foot came to rest, and its reluctance to leave as her prehensile toes lifted and moved forwards. She opened her mouth and drew in smooth, silky air, sharp on the back of her throat, and felt it swirl with her blood through her body, up to her head and cascading along her arms to her expectant fingertips.

The vibrant orange eye in the serene blue sky bubbled with energy, its flames leaping over the sea of life spread beneath it. Its power seemed to urge her on; I give you life, feel it, be it. On impulse she lifted her dress over her body and let it slip through her fingers onto the ground. Her every limb became aware of the air, of the way it encased her yet allowed her to swim obliviously through it. She experimented with the life in the branches of her body, watching her slender arm move away from her side and rise to the sky, her fingers dancing with elation. All the time aware of the liquid air, creamy against her naked pink flesh, her arm became part of nature; disconnected from modesty.

Curiously she felt the coat of nudity that she wore, playing with the tiny hairs that so looked like the grass she stood in. Her hand explored further along the path of her arm to her shoulder where the skin stretched over the bones of her body, their closeness forming crests and shallows that were exciting and pleasing to discover. Eventually her hands met at the nape of her neck, and after seeming to converse for a moment, agreed to daringly venture on down her warm youthful front in search of more of the wonders of life. They pondered over her small, firm breasts that tingled with delight at being found, her deep pink nipples hard in the cool air. She marvelled at her sexuality; she was in a woman's body, she had the ability to carry, nurture and feed a baby. She was essential to nature; the human form needed her to sustain its being.

Her hands carried on, stroking on over her downy flat stomach to her navel. She fondled it for a moment, feeling the depth of the magical crater before running her finger in a line down to her bed of mossy black pubic hair. This is where it happens, she thought, through the forbidden fleshy folds of feminine skin between her supple golden thighs. This is sensation, this is life.

She lay in the tongues of grass and writhed around feeling it lick all of her body. I am alive, she thought, and I am a wonder of creation.

*My Mum

The long brown hair of my mother,
So straight and knot free,
Like that of a curtain tassel.
Her long agile fingers,
Part her hair into three equal partings,
Shimmering in the light,
Just like a ripple in a pool.
She places each shiny parting,
So delicately,
On top of each other.
The once straight hair,
Is quickly turned into a line,
Of flowing curves,
As lovely as the curves,
Of the petals on a flower.
The quickness and speed,
Of the plait being made,
Is like that of a cheetah chasing a hare,
And sprinting straight past you.
Then the end of the plait disappears,
As she pulls it in front of her.
Looking into the mirror,
A perfectly still pool of water,
Standing up straight and tall,
You can see a hair band,
Like a python,
Closing round on its prey.

The twang of the band,
Like an elastic band,
Being pulled,
On a margarine tub guitar.
Then the intriguing magic of the plait,
Is over.

Polly Playford (12)

Alexandra Laight (7)

*Love

You could fall in love at a shop like Home-Base or Tescos. But then you have to ask them if they are married or something because if they are married you might get into a fight or something.

Say you're shopping and you haven't got a wife (you're not really looking for a woman). Well, you could say "Aaaahh", she looks beautiful by the looks, the hair, she might be a blonde, she has nice jeans, nice shirt, she might have nice perfume on, she isn't mucky, she has nice lovely eyes, mascara and eye shadow, nice red rosy cheeks, and a nice nose like my mums for instance, and nice skin that feels nice. It could happen with anyone. A woman might think a man has: nice hair, (we don't want grey hair do we!) No lipstick, some nice freckles – not spots! A nice sort of feeling, your feeling inside that a man is quite nice.

Well now let's go on to the other thing I wanted to say.

What I thought of love, when I was little. I used to think that there was a big forest with lots of men around. And the lady looked around for men and asked them "excuse me but what do you feel about me and are you married?"

You can have love between a little girl and a mommy or nanny. If you love someone you don't absolutely have to like them, because sometimes you can hate them sometimes and love them other times. And love can be done by two grown men and two grown ladies.

They said that in Waynes World.

I know a lot about love and stuff.

Well, people said Rajan and I were in love. Well we weren't but we really liked each other a lot and we were really really good friends.

We were in nursery, in Mrs Palmer's and Mrs Johnson's and then he left.

"I couldn't believe it."

Now I'm really sad he has gone, (to London), because he was my bestest friend ever.

I know a lot about love because I have got a boy friend. Martin Fenn's brother Chris (an N.C.T. friend)

"I'm in a world of my own" thats what Miss Anstis says.

Well, you see love is like a beauty.

It's like you feel really happy.

It's like a world of your own with just you and your boy-friend.

I'd like two volunteers to say what they think about love. I shall ask them what does it feel like to be in love with someone.

I'd like to pick out Belinda and Nicholas because they are in love with each other. They are seven years old.

Love can even stand between a one year old and a three year old like my sister and me who should really know better.

I saw that on the video when she rolled me on the floor and my mum said "stop it".

You see we keep little records on the video so we can see what happened years ago.

I think it was in 1987 when I was born.

It is about our N.C.T. friends, ourselves and cousins and grandma and nanny Peggy –

(nanny Peggy is dead now).

You can be in love with somebody even if they are not your real parents.

If you are stuck in an orphanage, sometimes the man and

the lady come and they think how lovely you look and they love you and you're really happy.

They choose you by how lovely you are. They keep you for a week or so and check how good you are, if they like you they keep you and if they don't they take you back.

They might take you from a small age.

But it's hard to cope with small children.

So they'd probably choose them from a bigger age.

If they are bigger they take a scrap or so from the fridge. It's easier because they can feed themselves.

You can love animals, they are very nice to keep. I could have a puppy, a rabbit, any baby animal.

I wouldn't like a baby crocodile if it growed up in my room it would be eating parts of me every day. I would like a horse. Actually I'd like a donkey. They are like retired ponys or horses or mules they are grey on top and walk really slowly. Because I don't like things that gallop or trot because I might fall off them.

If you write love poems to people it shows how beautiful they are:

> your cheeks are like roses
> your eyes are like peaches
> your nose is really soft
> your hair is beautiful.

but of course it doesn't have to rhyme.

actually you could write your penpal if you love them.

Romance

romance means that you go to a really private restaurant, or get a chinese take away (not like Mcdonalds) and have a nice meal if you've booked it.

I've got five top tips:

1 be smooth
2 never say horrible, disgusting words to them.
3 Show that you respect her or him and will look after
  them till death do us part.
4 take them for a dance or to a restaurant or an outing that
  will prove that you really think she is beautiful.
5 Write poems or cards or a story to her or him.

that's my top five tips.

because thats all you need for them to know that you really
like them.
  you could send a painting to show that she is beautiful.
  you can't send one through the photo-copier. the glass
might break if you're sending it through the post I warn you!
  the painting le-Repos by Picasso shows how beautiful a
woman could look. the hands are not very well joined
together but I warn you that I can't draw hands very well
either.

Lets go on from that point.
  I would like to tell you and show you somethings that
mean love.
  I have brought in a book of art that has got a picture of
artistry like love "the sign of love!" I have also got at home
a lovely sign of love painting.
  Just because it was in a glass frame I couldn't bring it and
it was so precious.
  It's called The Lunch and it was done by Claude Monet
and the painting shows people going to a wedding and having
a tea-party.

I've just tried to explain love I've tried as hard as I can. But engagements and weddings are all I can see in love.

But here comes the kissing part. I would like Belinda Daw and Nicholas Herlihy to come up here and do that part of acting.

Now the end of the Wedding. You may now kiss the bride.

There are just a few more questions I'd like to ask you.

These are my questions.

1 What is love all about? (Love, engagements and weddings when people get married).
2 What were the pictures I described about and what was the person's names who did them (Love: Picasso – Le Repos, and Claude Monet – The Lunch).
3 Name two of my tips (be smooth, write poems).
4 What happens when you're in an orphanage?
5 What did I think when I was young about how people went to find men or women to fall in love with?

Thank you for listening to my talk. Have you got any questions?

That's my report about love.

Good afternoon.

Hudheifa Akber Moawalla (13)

*Grace for Chinese Food

Praise thee, for the Chinese men and women who love to
    delight
People with endeavourous attitudes are worthy of rolling
    the Pancake up,
The Singapore noodles are the lungs of the meal,
The Peking duck, vegetables and plum sauce,
But laud and magnify the pancake which rounds off the
    mouth –
Crying course.
Chinese tea, warm but tasteless, unlike the rest of the
    savoury meal,
The last supper: would I eat a better supper again?
Praise thee, tenderfoots, who appreciate new tastes and
    ways.

Amy Evans (15)

*Hey! Evan, Man
(or "An Ode to Evan Dando of the Lemonheads")

Some girls, they fancy hunks
"Have you seen his chest?" they say
"Amazing upper body. Twenty inch biceps."
Oooh. How sexy
But I say I like a man with a lemon head
He don't need to wax his chest
He can sing and play the gee-tar

Some, they say they don't understand
"It's a Shame About Ray?" they say,
"Who's Ray? Is he gay?"
But Evan man, he don't say
"Listen Without Prejudice"
He say "Hey! that's cool."
He's no bitter lemon.

Some, they say "He won't take your name if you marry"
But he like them to say
"Hey! You Evan Evans man!"
He'll laugh
Hur! Hur! Hur!
Without even moving his mouth

Some, they say "You silly girl"
But I tried many fruits
Grape Apple Mango Peach
But I could find my heaven with Evan
So I say "Hey! Evan, man!
Come lay your head in my fruit bowl."

Alice Hutcheson (14)

Katie Brown (15)

*Sunflower

He lay waking slowly in the
Studio flat
As warm sun streamed gently
Through the windows softly smudged with
Finger prints

It was early morning and
The subdued mute of piano music
Seeped like syrup into the room
From the flat below.

26

He smiled himself awake
As the flame-yellow petals of the sunflowers
In the jam jar by the door
Curled at the edges
And the wood-brown seeds
Scattered across the
Sun-gold floor boards.

The city outside the window
Began to flash its
Electric impulses
In soft reverence of the warm morning
And he lay still
Wrapping himself drowsily
In that London sound.

The delicate perfume
Of the fading flowers
Coloured the dust motes beyond
With its pale balm
And the sun threw gradual gleams,
Like sherbet lemons,
Into the room
Rippling the planes of the window frames
And turning to liquid as it
Fell on all his records.

The sunflower's petals
Fell heavily and clumsily to the floor,
Turning mere wood to fields of burnished August corn.

As far across the London meadows
The day began.

Saad Choudhary (14)

*His Friend

It was possible and he read it.
It was impossible and he read it.
There was time and he read it.
There was no time and he read it.

The print was small and he read it.
The print was large and he read it.
The cover was interesting and he read it.
The cover was boring and he read it.

The book was boring and he read it.
The book was exciting and he read it.
He was sad and he read it.
He was happy and he read it.

Others were interested and he read it.
Others were not interested and he read it.
The day was bright and he read it.
The day was dark and he read it.

His father was drunk and he read it.
His mother was drunk and he read it.
His father hit him and he read it.
His mother hit him and he read it.

It was his only friend.
His only luxury.
And once the last page was finished.
He put it down with tears in his eyes.

GRASS STAINS AND GRAZES

Emily Ross (13)

The Forbidden Sweet

Are you interested in a tale of a girl who had no right to be punished? You are? Good. It begins in the light of the day . . .

Susie Bondoonser was going to fetch a paper when she saw it. It was lying on the grass, near a rubbish sack that somebody had split open. Slowly Susie debated whether to pick it up or not. "Shall I? Yes. NO. I can't. Yes. NO. Yes. No." Finally; "All right. It can't be poisonous." She picked it up and carried on to the Newsagents.

At school Susie was all alone. She sat on the wall and put her hands in her pockets. Then she felt that terrible sweet that was going to do all sorts of horrible deeds to her. It tasted of cinnamon. Ugh. She hated cinnamon. She swallowed it quickly. A feeling of guilt spread over her. She went indoors with the other children, still with the guilt.

Then a Very Funny Thing Happened. Susie grew fatter! Miss Brenning was suddenly, astonishingly squashed.

Susie was thin.

She was tall.

She was mouse-size.

Miss Brenning screamed. "Roderick! Cyril! Fetch the school nurse!"

Roderick Fletcher and Cyril Bindon sped off.

Susie was flat.

The school nurse and two teachers came. Miss Brenning nearly fainted. Susie was giraffe-like. Somebody fetched a stretcher. Rory Jones telephoned the Ambulance. The Nurse and a teacher struggled, almost letting go of the stretcher at times.

At the Hospital Susie turned green. She was given a bucket.

She turned blue. She was put in the oven.

She turned red. She was put in the freezer.

When she was having an injection the doctor was injecting a mouse. A very tall neck with a stump of a body. A gorilla. A monkey.

One doctor said it was the infection of Athparagustintomo. Another said it was quaintidalfangodolp, a third zambolic-diquarium.

In the end they decided on the rare, rare, famous goose-pimples-over-doing-it-infection. Ha, Ha. I'm laughing. No the Ambaldo infection. (Very rare.)

Then last of all Suzie went pink, red, blue, green, yellow, purple, silver, gold and went up, down, from side to side, went small, fat, then finally gave a roar that filled every corner of the hospital. The doctors decided on Thamin-gamble.

And all this was because of one tiny sweet.

Benji Scarlett (8)

Adventure Playground

There's an adventure playground
in my dinner where
battered sausage children
fill water pistols
from my tea;
little chip children
slide down the cup handle,
play football with my beans,
swing on strings of cheese and
use bits of lettuce as parachutes.

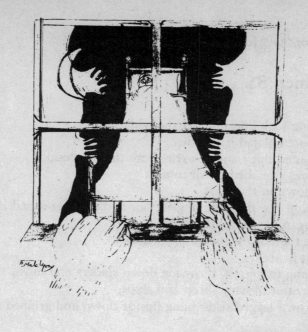

Darius Malekpour (13)

Rosalind Holden (6)

*Dreams

When I get into bed at night,
I place my dolls and teddies around me.
My dolls catch the small nightmares
and the teddies catch the big ones.
The King Teddy keeps them all
in a shoe box in the cupboard.
He is the only one big enough to do it.
In the morning, my teddies throw
the bad dreams in the dustbin.

Alexandra McRae (15)

Summer '85

Standing scab-kneed under the wide sky
We contemplated it together.
It sprouted thick and towering into the fat clouds,
Its leaves stretched down to us.
I lay down in the grass,
Watching her, through tangled hair and summer-dazed eyes.
She began to climb, bare-foot;
Where the boughs joined like knuckles,
She sat in shorts
And sang to herself, throwing down spiders and moss.
As I dreamt of hazy sheep and ships,
My brown-legged sister hung upside down and grinned at
    me.

When she slithered down
She brought grass stains and grazes
To be carried home like prizes, with
The lunchbox and myself.

Benjamin Grunberg (8)

My Papa

My papa picks me up,
From school,
Without my mum knowing,
And takes me to his house,
He pats me on my neck,
Saying "Ochky Buchky",
All the time,
He once told me,
It means, "I love you".
He puts presents by
Our bed, when we stay there,
On Fridays,
My Sister is papa's birthday present,
He always wears cashmere.
Today I feel,
Lonely, scared and guilty,
Because he is dead.

Laura McIvor (14)

My Grandmother

Friday night. That was granny night. That was our night. I looked forward to it all week long, looked forward to chocolate doughnuts and Tizer, consumed on my own little stool in front of the fire. We would sit together with the lights off, watching out of the large back window as the hedgehogs and foxes passed through the garden, our nightly visitors. The hedgehog scurrying along like a timid little mouse, lapping up milk from the saucer my grandmother had left for it, but ready to deliver a nasty sting to any who dared get too close, and the fox slipping stealthily in and out of the many shadows cast by bushes. Then I would go to my bed. My gran would have had the electric blanket on to heat my bed, and she would spread my pyjamas out on the mattress so that they would absorb the rising warmth. Then she would tuck me up snuggly in the thick downy, my head nestling in the deep pillows, and kneel beside the bed to say my prayers with me. Her kind blue eyes would close as she murmured her words of belief, the eyes that had seen so much.

She was born and grew up in Cootehill, County Cavan, in Eire, on a farm. She was very poor, and seldom had enough to eat. Her father died when she was still young, bled to death outside the protestant houses, because he was a catholic. Since they no longer had a "man of the house" the council came to evict them, a widow with her little children, but the IRA heard of these plans and put a stop to them. Thus they did not lose their farm. My gran then came over to Edinburgh to work, leaving her family behind. She walked to work at the Royal Edinburgh Hospital every day and sent almost all of her wages home to her mother to help keep the wee ones fed. It was at her work that she met my granddad.

My grandmother had a lovely, soft Irish accent, and still spoke the way she had in Ireland, stringing beautiful words together into sentences that strangers to her tongue could not always understand, and even now my father and his brothers often lapse into this dialect.

Like a lot of people who grew up with hunger, my granny always tried to feed people up. She loved to spoil me and loved me no matter what ghastly feat I had done. In the mornings when I padded through to the living room her softly wrinkled but still beautiful face would greet me and we would sit in front of the window watching the rest of the world wake up, and as our day-time friends filed in, she would go and put the respective food in the respective places; nuts up the tree for the birds, and, if they were crafty, the squirrels; catfood down for the cat with the bell on its collar. Then we would wait and laugh at the antics. The green tits batting at the blue tits with their tiny wings to get at the nuts, the starlings and the thrushes chasing the smaller birds away when they became hungry and the plain blackbird waiting for an opportune moment to dive in and nab a nut. In between mouthfuls the birds would assemble in the branches of the tree and sing their thanks to us, their throats pulsing with the effort of reaching higher notes than all the others. My favourite bird was the robin red breast which put in occasional appearances. Sometimes doves would come, but that was very rare. They were Granddad's birds. They would sit on his shoulders and eat from his hands, but when he departed they did also. There would be pheasants strutting around the garden, the male displaying his impressive plumage to its best advantage. These and many others fascinated me.

When I had finished breakfast and gone away to wash, my grandmother would sit hunched up in front of the fire heating my clothes for me and once dressed we would toddle off to the corner shop to buy a paper and invariably Granny would buy me a packet of sweeties. Sometimes we would buy a bag of our peppermint sweets and suck them.

After lunch on Saturday we would play dominoes together or I would get out the little suitcase with the cars in it and tirelessly wheel them around the room as she smiled or took her pills. She had a heart condition (Angina) and survived on numerous multi-coloured tablets, some long, some fat, which she took several times a day. In the early afternoon one of my parents, usually my dad, would come and collect me. Sometimes I would make a fuss about going home and would get a row, but my grandmother would always stick up for me, telling my father to "leave the good child alone" (the good child being me), and I would tell her about the naughty things my father had done recently and she would jokingly warn him "you're never too big to go over my knee."

My grandmother's bedroom was like a shrine to me, full of intriguing corners and pictures. On her dressing-table she had a big powder puff and a swivel mirror which was normal on one side and magnified if you looked at the other. She had pearls and talc and perfume and brooches and tucked underneath was a white stool which twirled round. On her bureau she had all of her rosary beads and holy water and pictures and a huge statue of the Blessed Virgin Mary in a glass case. That was my favourite. It is supposed to represent Mary appearing to Bernadette at Lourdes. My granny had a very strong catholic faith. She went to mass every day, prayed every night and taught me a lot about God. She did not doubt that there was a heaven and that, when she died, she would be reunited with my grandfather, and nor did I. When my granddad died, my grandmother lost the will to live. All she wanted was to be with him again. She carried a photo of him with her everywhere she went and never got rid of the second bed in her room, as if she thought granddad might want to sleep there. I do not remember my granddad because he died when I was just going on four.

Sometimes during the summer I would ride a tricycle around the back patio, pedalling furiously to keep the stiff little wheels turning, and when I eventually got fed up and came inside there would be an ice-lolly and a bowl waiting for me, and we would go down to the bottom of the garden to pick fruit, granny and I. There were raspberries, black currants, gooseberries and rhubarb, but I always chose to collect the strawberries. There was not much point in bothering to collect peas-in-the-pods because every time my cousins and I visited we would raid these plants, tearing open the pod and munching the sweet peas ruthlessly. She always had pots of jam to give away and freshly baked rhubarb and apple tarts, the fruit for which came from the garden. She undertook the trying task of teaching me to knit, demonstrating a patience I could not muster.

At Christmas the McIvor family congregated at her house to exchange gifts, talk and laughter, but more importantly, to dine. Huge meals would be presented and enjoyed. Roast turkey with stuffing, gravy, cranberry sauce, roast potatoes, mashed potatoes, broccoli, carrots, chipolatas wrapped in bacon and brussel sprouts made up one course out of four. I looked forward to Christmas because it was a time of the whole family gathering, whether it was my mother's or my father's side.

I remember that Christmas well. I had made a little brooch for granny, from some holly leaves and berries, and I knew she would love it because it was the work of my hands, if perhaps a little crude. That morning we were all up, getting ready for work and school respectively, and the phone rang.

My day shattered before my eyes. Granny had had a heart attack and was in hospital. Mum and dad rushed out. All I could do was sit and pray.

The three of us – my sister, Marcia, my brother, Scott, and I – sat immersed in our own thoughts, waiting for what we hoped would be good news although I think we all knew it was futile even before our parents came back and told us. It is the only time I have ever seen my father cry. With one morning's anxious wait the lady I had loved beyond all love was gone forever. No more Friday nights. When we went to see her, I pinned my Christmas brooch on her, afraid to kiss the cold, sallow cheek.

Death had never even crossed my mind. I was young and innocent and the tub of tablets carried no significance for me. She was my very own guardian angel, soft, kind, gentle, protecting, caring, loving, warm, generous. When she died I cried, and with those salty tears I lost some of my trust in God. I had prayed so much for her and He had taken her away. I became very bitter. Now, though I accept that she is happier with my grandfather, God is not the same to me. I know she went straight to heaven, carried by the goodness and love she doled out to others and the love others felt for her, and although I know her body is buried fifteen feet in the ground, I often look up at the sky at night, at the biggest, brightest star, the brightest star up there radiating light, and as it twinkles at me I raise my arm and wave, wave to my grandmother.

Stephanie Reynolds (7)

*Jealousy

Jealousy is dark blue.
Jealousy is when Samuel
is getting a cuddle
And I'm
on the settee without one.
Jealousy sounds like crying and huffiness.
Jealousy tastes sour in your throat.
Jealousy smells like sweat and sort of strange.
Jealousy feels like you have two hearts,
One going up in anger,
And one going down with sadness.

Alex Huff (16)

Jenny Haydock (14)

Early Days

Our classroom was separated from Mr Palmer's by
A row of drawers where we kept work and
A chipboard screen where we displayed our
"Pictures of Initials" of which the best was
Tanya Smith's, of course, who was so jealous when I was
May Queen even though I did have to dance with
Paul Taylor when I wanted to dance with
Simon who couldn't even write his name when I was as far as
Joined-up writing and knew all my
Tables which were up on the wall by
Mrs Roper's desk which she sat on during our
Spelling tests which Derek always failed but
Mrs Roper didn't give him
Blue cards which I never got yet
Jodie got more than one a week but she was still my
Best friend in the whole world and was vice-chairman of the
"Grassy Club" whose members collected
Pollen and planted grass seeds on the
Playground where I first finished "elastics" and kissed
David who hated it like I hated
Fleur who drew on my drawer label and laughed at
Jodie who just laughed back when Fleur pulled her
Dragon from the ceiling and then pretended
I had done it so I said she looked like the
Toad which we once had to draw to go on the screen for
Nature study and one morning Mrs Maynard, who taught
5S, pulled back the screen and said in a
Sorry voice that we all knew

Margaret Lockwood who was in
4C and she wasn't in
School today because her mummy had been ill and had
Left us.
Everyone was quiet for a long time.
I remember wondering where she had gone to because
She was always puffing when I saw her, like the
Steam engines which we drew for a project on
Machines for which we also studied
Aeroplanes and Simon said his
Dad flew one for the Air Force and went to
Africa and other places far away and
I decided to be a
Pilot when I was older and fly planes with
Simon but then he announced one day he loved
Fleur, so I hated him from then on.
That's all I remember.

               *   *   *

It was all a long time ago.
The voice in my head urges,
"Try to look forward, to what lies ahead",
But I can't help envying the
Child who knew so little of the world,
Who could brush away the
Hurt and pain and
Carry on so easily with
Such innocence.
Blessed naivety.

**Heartland

It was a violently sunny day, the bright sunlight spilling in waves over the coast. The bay captured the light, distorted and reflected it so that from the sea the greens, reds and yellows of the hillside danced like carnival streamers. It was nearing harvest-time, and most of the locals were either in their fields or hiding from the heat in pebble-like houses sprinkled over the slopes. Therefore the long ribbon of smooth, vanilla sand that hugged the cliffs was almost deserted and the only activity seemed to be in a tiny cove tucked into the shoreline, where there sparkled what appeared to be a dirty-pink waterfall. In this place the soft chalk had been hewn away, exposing the brown boulders underneath. The rocks were embedded with tiny rose-quartz crystals which seemed to emanate pink light, with a spectacular effect; a mineral downpour frozen in mid-descent. It was here, on the round apron of sand below, that the boy was sitting. Heavily suntanned and wearing nothing but his khaki shorts he had been sitting here quite still for at least twenty minutes, listening to the cool, clear waves fizzing along the shore and feeling the heavenly heat soaking into his bones. At last he stirred, ruffled his sunbleached hair and rolled onto his back so that he could stare at the deep blue sky. Frothy clouds, painted purple and gold by the ultraviolet, drifted across. A caravan of travellers, or kingdoms . . .

He sighed. He liked this place. The sand was always clean, freshened every night when the sea stole up to kiss the jewelled skirts of the shore; and then of course there were the pretty shells, and the strange rocks – when he had time he would bring his father here. He fished in his pocket and retrieved his sunglasses, which he put on ceremoniously. "California 509's – the original eyeware!" he proclaimed in a fake American accent, and burst into raucous laughter. Falling abruptly silent he solemnly sprinkled sand onto each brown lens until his vision was obscured, then folded his hands across his stomach and lay completely still. Maybe this was what dead people saw, looking up through the crumbling earth . . .

"Noah!"

He sat up slowly, allowing the sand to trickle down his face in two streams of sandy sorrow. Then he shut his eyes and tried to ignore the distant voice but, mosquito-like, it buzzed thinly, persistently in his ear. Saskia did not know for certain where he was – if he pretended that he hadn't heard, that he was too far away to hear, she would never know. But she would guess. Furiously he stood up, removed his glasses, carefully replaced them in his pocket and made his way back to the house.

Higher up, the church of St. Gabriela de Marqueza gleamed like a white tooth set in the hillside, and its pious bell tolled three o'clock for anyone who cared to hear. He looked up, giving it a friendly wave, and felt a little better. He had run down the path but clipped his speed to a deliberately casual gait as he approached the villa, then sauntered around the house to the rear courtyard and stepped into the kitchen.

The room was deep and cavernous, and so dark that it made his eyes tingle. Grey stone floor and speckled grey walls, with stalwart cedar furniture; all hung with oblique blue shadows. Draped in its shadowy coolness, looking out at the sun-baked courtyard was like being inside a giant granite eye and staring out at another world. Usually a hive of smells and activity, the kitchen seemed wistful in its emptiness. He turned to leave – no Saskia here – but was drawn to investigate a heap of purple stuff lying on the table.

Grapes! Noah flew over and gazed greedily at the large wooden dish piled high with bunches. If he was quick he could help himself, and Saskia would never notice . . . hearing faint footsteps in the hallway he seized two handfuls and rushed back out into the sunlight.

Safely round the corner, he paused to examine his spoils. The grapes were typical of the region, passionately purple and beautifully round. They were fine specimens; holding them up to the light he could see that their glistening skins were unblemished and heavy with juice. Still joyfully absorbed in his fruit he wandered down the grassy verge and onto the red path leading into the woods.

Shady and humid in the heat, with only a few diamonds of light piercing the tapestry of boughs, the woods brimmed with the sweet stink of Summer rot. The mossy floor here rose and fell in tiny hills and valleys. Parties of scarlet and orange flowers congregated under low shrubs, and wilted daintily; sly, olive-green vines wrapped themselves a path to the few patches of visible sky. Noah lay sleepily in the arms of a low tree. He had eaten the grapes slowly, placing them on his chest and twisting them off one by one. His fingers were drenched in their warm, sweet juice and he was quite, quite full. He wondered what the time was, then remembered that he still had not found Saskia. He sat up guiltily, swung down and bent to wipe his hands on the grass . . .

It was then that he saw the snake. Only two yards away, an emerald girdle coiled round a tree trunk, it rested in the damp heat. The crimson V on its crown shone dangerously. Noah froze immediately; watching, waiting. He must stay still, very still, and wait for it to move away. These were the deadly creatures that the locals always spoke of and feared; "You see one, kill him quickfast!" But this was his first encounter with one and in a strange way he did not mind being bound here by its poisonous spell. Its glistening skin fascinated him, those dark, insidious eyes; and what cruel, elegant thoughts was it thinking? This outcast duke had sought refuge here among the stinking roots, away from Man's senseless commotion. Yet it seemed to shun his pity with its steady poise. Then slowly, oh so slowly, the snake began to uncoil and descend the trunk . . .

Suddenly Noah was tearing away through the trees and back towards the house, shrieks of terror catching in his throat as he bounded over stones and ferns. Sharp twigs clawed his face as he rushed into the clearing and onto the path. But he did not see the second snake, brown and thick, and it snared his legs so that he tumbled, yelling, into the long grass.

Noah wrestled fiercely with the snake and slung it off into the grass where it lay motionless; the "snake" was only a length of dry rope. He laughed nervously, relieved, and sidled over to examine his assailant. Completely fibrous. He kept on laughing as he walked up the path towards the villa, in an effort to compose his racing mind, and just in case anyone had been watching. Why had he run off so quickly? But it would have gone now. A real snake, like the ones in encyclopaedias only better because it had really been there, right there, so green and still and quite, quite beautiful. And highly deadly; and his sister would probably have died if she had seen it. His first real taste of danger!

"It must be about four o'clock by now," he mused, "and Father said that he'd be back by four." As if on cue, the church clock struck out four tinny chimes. Noah whooped loudly:

"Ye-hes! A most palpable hit, Nonny-boy!" and he galloped triumphantly towards the house, to see if his father was home.

Christopher Stopher (13)

Thresholds

Are lines of hesitation,
And desperation,
Placed directly and firmly,
Like road markings.
They wait for the one
Who over steps the mark.
But my foot steps,
Are scared and shaking,
Like a tuning fork.
I jump the threshold
Landing on the fake ceramic tiles;
The walls are full of paintings,
Clowns glaring and donkeys in deep meadows.
The smell of semolina and carrots
Wafts down the corridor
On warm thermals.
I walk
My feet squelch,
Like plungers.
I come to the door,
And my heart beats
In an eerie silence,
Until the teacher says,
"Who are you?"
My throat dries up.
I answer "Chris, Miss."
She takes me by the arm,
And sits me in my place,
Where the knots in the wood

Stare at me like curious eyes.
They begin to cry,
Flash tears.
I look away,
Then back,
And the eyes are knots again.
I smell Copydex, like scampi.

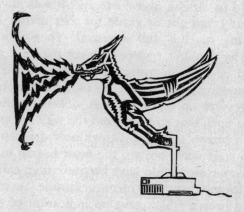

Alec Storey (12)

And the Over Head Projector,
Is an angry dragon,
Breathing fire onto the board
Where the shadowy letters
Are singed,
And begin to crumble,
Like old cement.

The chalk cascades into mystery
Which is held in the future,
Where my primitive past
Reads the writing on the wall.

Saad Choudhary (14)

*Unwanted Pressure

I wasn't sure. I stared at it. It was like a chance card, only what was inside was not chance. That's what made it terrible.

It would be alright, above average. It was always alright. Any report I had got or grade for that matter had always received my parents' full approval. They thought I was superb, why couldn't I agree? To say they put pressure on me would be a lie. In truth, all the pressure on me was of my own making. I was maybe the only teenager in the world to put pressure on myself. It was sickening, the amount I wanted to open that envelope and the way I stopped myself.

It was a brown envelope. Brown how depressing. What a colour to start with, brown, the most boring in the world. What was outside should have been exciting, exhilarating to make up for the customary blemishes inside. Yet it was boring and bland brown which gave no indication of the material inside. It was so neutral, so typical, so average, the opposite to what I wanted. I felt like turning away but the envelope glared at me. I stared at it again.

Just the mere envelope reminded me of the twelve or so teachers that taught me. It was as if that inconsequential envelope was each of their faces grinning at me. So much power given to one person to create or destroy another person's hopes and dreams. Teachers were expected to be machine-like and mark in an unbiased and perfect way, only machines could do that.

It now seemed as if the envelope was my master and it was the one that was six foot tall. At that time the envelope seemed to be more likely to swallow me up than for me to rip it apart.

I picked up the forbidden envelope that was causing me so much distress. I began to run my finger along the paper to see what was really so fearsome about it. It was so smooth, so perfect, inviting me to open it yet I couldn't. My original happiness about getting the report was long since gone and I wished to throw it away and do something more interesting. I pictured the report and knew the consequences of opening it were far less threatening than I made them seem.

My parents had always told me that whatever I did was fine by them. I had been told repeatedly by friends, family and teachers that this worrying did no good. I knew myself that it did not help but could not stop somehow. I always worked as hard as I could and a bit harder than that as well, therefore I should always have been confident. I don't know why but I grew up believing that worrying was the best policy. This was a major weakness and one that was infuriating for me as well as everyone else.

Some people had said to me that this worrying about my grades was arrogance; this hurt me because nothing was further from the truth. The only reason I worried was because of a lack of confidence in my abilities. Some had reasoned that this was because of my ethnic roots but I did not feel this at all. In fact I was upset if someone treated me as special because this was an unfair burden.

I had been called many names before, "sad" and "square" included. This was mainly because I didn't hide anything while others far more ambitious than me would censor their speech and personality so as to create a popular image for themselves. As I have said I am not square but my uncensored natural manner made others feel I was.

If the people who thought I was arrogant saw me before a lesson they would see the opposite but that would be my real personality. I would be worried, confused, gullible and totally unhappy. Sometimes I worried myself sick over a particular lesson.

I looked at my watch and saw that I had been sitting in the same position just thinking for almost half an hour. Even now I was no nearer to even considering opening the envelope.

I always likened things to my beloved Greek mythology and unwittingly I slipped into a dream world. I dreamt of sitting in a meadow many thousands of years ago. I had been given a gift and was wondering whether to open it or not. Then Hermes the glittering messenger of the Gods came from heaven and told me to open it. I wanted not Hermes but someone else to make a similar kind of intervention.

No one came but I escaped back to reality. This was part of the problem, I lived in a world that was a bit far fetched. The fact that I was not able to open a report when I could be sure that next to each subject would be either a big, fat **A** an equally large **B** or an occasional **C** was almost unbelievable. I could be told by a teacher that a piece of work was very good but I could still find a million faults with it. I would never hand in a piece of work without having a criticism about it. This could be something as simple as a comma when there should have been a full stop.

I would have to open the report before my parents came home. They would want me to open it and stop worrying about it and rightly so.

I slowly withdrew one hand from my pocket and touched the smooth brown exterior that haunted me so much. For a while I just sat and held the envelope thinking, seeing and hearing nothing. Then slowly, almost painfully, I opened the envelope. Each movement of my finger was another unknown feeling until finally the report lay before me.

I took the white sheet of paper from the jaws of the envelope and unfolded the report again slowly, very slowly. I looked at the report, my eyes hopping from subject to subject then finally counting all the grades. There were five

A's and three B's. A shout of triumph was about to pass from my lips, but then I caught a glimpse of the general comment. It said "a little inconsistent". For most this would have been an indication to work harder more consistently, to me it was a sign that I was not good enough. It made me feel sick, the excellent grades disappeared. All that was left was inconsistency. As I looked around it was as if inconsistent was printed on the walls and more importantly it was imprinted in my brain. I could not forget it and the short moment of happiness after reading my grades had long since passed.

I lay down on my bed totally dejected and lay there staring into space for a little while. I then directed my thoughts to school the next day. I would as usual stride past everyone in the class and go and sit with the squares popularly known as the sad patrol. While everyone in the class would sit and talk about normal fifteen year old things the sad patrol would talk about marks and job prospects. I had used to sit with the others and make fun of the squares. However I was always hesitant as in truth I admired the squares. Maybe seeing this the workaholics had made me an honorary member and now I was unhappier then I was before.

This top notch of society amazed me in every way. They were somewhat richer then the rest of us but not enough to go to a private school as I wished them to. Tomorrow they would sit in their customary circle and discuss their reports from dawn to dusk.

These most hated people were named Liam, Don and Henry and they were the lowest of low people I had met. While at home and at parties they may have had the most exquisite of manners, at school they were non existent. While willingly joining them it now seemed insulting to be mentioned in the same breath as them. They may have been brilliant at everything but I did not care because they treated others like dirt and made my life hell. You could not put anything past them as they were so arrogant. They could even make fun of someone's home background.

Jon and Simon were the two I preferred, they were boys in the true sense of the word. They loved football, computers, videos or anything else that was fun. They had been upset that I had changed so much. They were much better people then the squares because they liked me for what I was not what my grades or possessions showed me to be. Jon and Simon offered me a lot more than the sad patrol. They offered me a chance to be myself. A chance I had to accept.

I then mentally stuck my middle finger up to the inhuman, ultra ambitious and egotistical people that had spoiled the last year of my life. I resolved not to talk to them, but to talk to Jon and Simon again.

That night as I reflected on the day's events, I knew a slow change had come over me. It was no sudden Hollywood transformation, more a slow realisation that set me on the right path again. I needed to live life again like a carefree, blunderbuss and idiotic fifteen year old. There were many years before I needed to contemplate the difficulties I had been contemplating for years. I was expected to live football, computer games and videos. Delights I had thought for only hooligans before.

17 May 1995 any old hot summer night for everyone around the world. A new beginning for my revitalised life. I fell asleep after doing my homework and watching Match of the Day and saw that I could combine the two. In my sleep I relived every minute of football, computers and videos all of which I had indulged in that day. Instead of the usual tests, dole queues and other grim thoughts which were safely locked away and might be opened in a decade's time or when I felt like it.

AS FAR AS THE ROAD IS LONG

Nathan James (16)

Maninder Singh (7)

*Playtime

At playtime I stuff my face
with prawn cocktail crisps.
I play "Double Dragon" by myself.
Kids say, "No, you can't play!"
Once, there was a huge crane
outside the playground, and
everybody crowded round the gate
shouting, "Pick me up! Pick me up!"

Eva Okwonga (16)

**A Letter for Ayatt

That was how it came. A secret flower of folded papers, each sheet as frail as old women's cheeks. The creased envelope, the colour of desert sands, bearing clumsy AirMail labels and two square stamps, one depicting a river, the other a purple-plumed bird. Half-way across the world, in planes and vans and trains, over forests and salt water, to sift itself through a letterbox and settle on carpet. From me to you. To here.

The cleaning staff were leaving the bright synth-reality of the office. On her way out Ayatt caught sight of herself in the mirrored walls, a chestnut figure in the chattering crowd. Muffled in her heavy jacket; her petticoat was rucked up between her polished skin and teacloth weave tunic; low, sensible shoes covered strong feet made to walk as far as the road is long. She critically smoothed down her braids, made untidy by the regulation caps they all wore. Good-bye, "Monroe and Sons". The strong, laced-up feet took on the midnight pavement, and the demure shoes squeaked suspiciously at the wrong end of a powerful stride. The walker glanced up at the passing sky, not expecting to see a panorama of African stars; nothing heavenly glittered in the vacant orange darkness that formed a sultry lid over the sprawling city. Most of the city's boiling incense burners, its cars and vans, were tamped down for the night but lead still tainted the frozen air. Threads of Congolese* music drifted out of a doorway, and Ayatt paused, curious, excited, outside the all-

* African dance music

night dive; but she saw lights, like electric serpents, pouring over clunking fruit machines, and the wrong kind of men. She walked on.

Ayatt was sitting in the underground carriage; with its graffitied red interior and broken seats, like a blasted theatre. The shabby man sat, inescapably, before her and she forced herself to return his sickly smile. He had spotted her, trying to read her A-level economics manual in the flickering light, and had joyfully told her that he too adored the subject and could explain, why, anything the Bank of England would throw you because *they* valued him, *very* highly; yes. He had upheld his monologue on subsidiarity for several minutes now. With every jolt of the carriage phlegm gurgled in his chest, and his brown teeth rattled as he garbled macro-economics. Ayatt slipped her hand into her coat pocket and took solace in the papery rustle she found there. Gripping her book in one hand, an unseen bustle of papers in the other, and she sat like this until Manor Park. "Come again soon?" whispered the man. She ran all the way to the round-about, and hoped that her aunt was home.

It was cold by the classroom window, cold, cold, cold, and a thin plate of frost had crept over the glass. Her concentration spoilt by the warm feeling inside her, Ayatt turned and gently rubbed herself an oval of clearness. Her finger gave up its warmth to the crispy opaqueness and she pressed the spot of chilled flesh to her cheek, while spying on the freezing world through her watch-hole. She smiled.

". . . and *when* Ayatt has returned to the lesson!" Mrs Trove, her economics teacher, smiled less warmly and viewed her with suspicion. At the end of the lesson she beckoned Ayatt aside while her classmates drifted outside.

"Ayatt." She folded her thin arms across her cardiganed body. "You really must concentrate, it is imperative, being not accustomed yet I think, and I will not tolerate . . ."

Oh yes but I have a wonderful reason yes today I got a letter from home not my real home but Kenya all the way from Kenya that's where we went because of the war and it was from my family can you believe it after three months it probably got lost I think wow! A letter of three sheets it was from my brother and do you know what my uncle is getting married I hope she is pretty. And I was so glad that I didn't even eat breakfast but I'm still not hungry even now that's how happy I am! I think . . . I think I miss them very much. But how can I explain this to you.

"I am just tired – I slept badly last night. No, language is no problem. Yes really. I understand."

The acidity of the wind round her legs horrified and hurried her. She walked through Rose Avenue, with its tidy semis and spotless Ford Escorts in each driveway. She wondered what kind of wallpaper these people had in their living rooms, and if they had dining rooms; but she hurried past and across the road to the council houses and now into Harbour Estate. Her natural balance navigated the bleeding Coke cans and grass-stuffed cracks in broken paving, while her mind warmed itself with memories of another, a heat-wavering life. As she rounded the corner to her street she imagined: four friends were running down a wide, baked road with the lazy applause of banana leaves above; now across the field, tall, heat-dried grass embracing their legs and above, an empty turtle-shell of blue. Conversation in an ancient language. "Did Lawino catch you? – Ha ha! I'm a professional and she runs like an elephant . . . – Mrs Odonga gave us three tests this week . . . – Look, look I can kick like Pele . . . – Is your father bringing the new goat today? – No, there's no market 'til Wednesday . . . – I hope Ecadu cut the grass . . ." Past a ghostly metropolis of termite hills and up and over the slope and onto the flatness around the waterpump . . .

This area was not as bad as some others, but she still felt uncomfortable here. A discarded newspaper had chased itself into their doorway and shouted something about taxes – trouble with peace treaties – a war in Africa. Into the hallway, where slippers were waiting on a strip of wine-coloured carpet with patterns of scallops. There was nobody home. Relieved to be back nonetheless, Ayatt passed into the kitchen, where the bulb screamed sharp light at the blue walls until they were white with fear. She quickly cleaned up, then wandered into the tiny living room and sat down on one of its spongy brown chairs. As she tidied up the papers on the coffee table she wondered how much colder it could get here, if it would snow – or was it too cold for snow now? Did Tesco's sell cheaper groceries? She did not think about the man on the train. The TV sat, unwatched, in the corner. Ayatt stared at its cold screen and now became aware of the silence of the empty house. She felt cold and a little weary. She wanted to – oh who knows? To get out? Some buildings have a soul, an energy borrowed from passing conversations, absorbed from rising laughter. But this house felt – dead. She tried to forget that this was her home now. She tried to smile as, for the sixth time that day, her fingers pulled out an envelope the colour of deserts. Her eyes roved over the inky blue crawl and once again received the news . . .

"Dear Ayatt,

How are you? As for me I am fine and so is Mama and Auntie Sophia and Omara and Uncle George. This is my number one letter and its in English. I think it is good. I like Auntie Sophia's house and Mtebo Town. We have a good school and we are studying very hard, just like you. I like

Maths and I like the school. There is a thermometer in Jino's Store and today it says 28°C. That's Celsius.

There is a tall mango tree in the front and our cousin Peter climbs it every day and takes the best ones. He is so fat. One day he climbed it and instead of a mango he found a big snake and it chased him across the compound. He ran to Auntie Sophia and she said he should not be so greedy and if he didnt remove the mango skins from his room he would find all the snakes friends under his bed too.

I went to big market with Uncle George and I had Fanta. Do you have Fanta in UK?

Uncle Olara is going to marry a lady from Tero Province next week and everybody is going. I am very excited. Every night we pray for you and Auntie and our beautiful country, united and free. 'Don't worry, be happy.'

    Yours sincerely
      Okech Samma – nine years old."

She did not read the bit from her mother which she knew by heart.

The letter was too short and her mind flooded with new questions now, all demanding attention.

It had arrived like a finger of liquid sun to probe her heart, to sample her new world for itself and give its honest opinion. "Don't worry, be happy." Perhaps it should have quietly lost itself on its long, long journey instead of coming here to pass sunny judgement and make its three-month absence felt.

She thought about the sky at home, so hard and wide and fiercely, deeply blue. The way it draped around the horizon. You could run out into the middle of the grass and for 360 degrees catch the warm wind blowing down from the hills. You could watch a bird until it disappeared from flying too far into the sphere. You could steal as many mangoes as you could carry and the trees would never notice, just nod a little less or creak from side to side in the sun. And weddings with such celebrations and music with beats as deep as the underground rivers that fed the old pump by their school. And her family . . . she stared at the page very hard and tried to deny the tears but they would come, salty streams running away from the sea that spread behind closed lids. To get out, to go home.

"Hello?"

Her aunt was home. For some reason, Ayatt sprang across the room and tried to hide herself in the farthest corner by the window, as though her aunt's scrutinizing gaze would turn her to dust or shame her in her sorrow. Auntie Biet flicked the light switch, annoyed:

"This girl! So wasteful!"

And went to bed.

So now she was alone again, in darkness, with her anger or guilt or whatever it was that she felt. And it was cold beside the window. The curtains shifted in the draught and a high moon tumbled a few coins of silver across her face. She cried for a while longer, letting the pearly tears spin from her face and down into the darkness. She should go to bed, move . . . But now the djinns of fatigue sat heavy on her mind and fragmented her thoughts with their glass hammers. 3.07 said the clock. The time for sleeping swarmed into her eyes and smoothed their lids into unconsciousness, leaning against the wall . . .

How far can you go, sister? Halfway across the world. As far as the road is long. But not without you.

"Good morning."

Someone was trying to draw the curtains.

"What time is it?'

"6.35am. Hey, have you been here all night?" It was Auntie

Biet. She was staring at Ayatt's crumpled uniform. "Are you feeling alright?"

"Yes, I'll be alright. Yes."

She wondered what she was doing here and then she saw the collection of airmail papers in her hand, crunched into a ball now. Had she had a bad dream? She resolved to write back as soon as possible; there was no address given but Auntie would know it. But what could she write about her overcast life here, in a house with no soul and a city full of crazy people?

"Auntie, do you have your sister Sophia's address? Auntie?"

And Auntie Biet was looking at the morning sky. Just . . . look. The sun was not yet visible above the cobbled horizon but the sky; look, an endless, cloudless swathe of electric-pink silk, blown out over the sluggish estates and wakening motorways. Aeroplane trails sparkled silver white like celestial fireworks streaking the ballooning softness, and even a few diamond-like stars clung persistently to the dawn. Things and people are thinking about their first movement of the day, but not yet, not until this shininess is dispersed, because this is . . .

"Amazing. How come – why is it like that? Will there be a storm or an eclipse or something?"

"No, it just does that sometimes," replied Auntie Biet. She shifted restlessly. "Don't be late." And left the room.

"Yes, I'll be alright." Ayatt sat there a little longer, still captivated. She would write back to her family. Ask for more news, pictures of the wedding even. Tell them about the sky here that turns itself inside-out just because it wants to.

"Are you going to lie there all day? Some people have work to do."

And letters to read. And write. Ayatt got ready for school.

Hudheifa Akber Moawalla (13)

*I Need this Touch of Home

Mortars, grinding chillies for the big night feast . . .

Here I am standing with a curry,
A dead curry;
Where are all the spices and chunks of vegetables floating
   on top
Of the grainy rice?

Anna Vickers (16)

If only I could see what was happening in Tanzania.
The smell of freshly laid-out cloves enrichening the smell
  of the
Atmosphere,
The lobster swimming on top of the waves of fire,
And the home-made dark yellow cheese acting like pulp
  on top
Of the browning lobster,
The High Street shops closing with small chatter.

Back to the barbecue!
The watotos playing cricket on the shore – soon to be called
  by their
Parents to eat.
I too am being called – but I am not there.

Perry Dhammika (5)

Adoption

I am a child of two worlds.
I was born in the African bush
but live in an English town
I like the town with shops
and no flies.
My mother likes the bush
all quiet with baboons
We come and go

María Thérèse Hogan (14)

*Into the Mountains

Mari rested in the shade of an old, gnarled tree near the school gates. Its branches hung low, practically brushing his dark face.

A fine dust swirled around the yard as the other boys ran up and down, kicking an ageing leather ball from one end of the pitch to another. Shouts and laughter filled the hot, stuffy air around the school.

Mari wiped his bare feet, which had become a dull grey with dust from the road; his brow was sticky with sweat and his face shone in the glaring light of the sun. He turned to face the sun, which hung high in the sky, an orange flare suspended in space. About three, he thought; soon he would be on his way home, to the village, and Ana. Ana was his wife, or at least, she would be one day, in the future. They had been betrothed at birth, and, being the only two children of their age in the village, they had grown up together, hardly been apart, until recently. Mari had been sent to a school far, far away from the village, while Ana, having reached her age, was kept at home.

Mari longed for the day when he and Ana would have their own home in the village, and he would be the head of a household.

Ana stood at the door of the hut, her younger brother in her arms, crying.

"Shh," she said, "hush babby, it's all right, nothing will hurt you here. See, the children are coming back from school, and mammy will soon be home."

She rocked him gently, cradling him in her arms, singing softly and swaying to the sweet lullaby.

The baby stopped crying, and, with a few quiet whimpers, closed his tiny eyes and fell fast asleep. Ana slowly walked into the hut and carefully placed him on to his blanket, stroking his small head as if to send him into an even deeper sleep.

What would her children be like? she wondered. She would love a little girl, who she could bring up on her own. A boy would be sent to school, or taken off by Mari to learn how to be a man. A girl however, would be left to her, be her responsibility and would grow up to have children of her own. Ana would be the mother of many then, for in her village, the mother of the mother was an important figure; not the head of the household, but the head of the whole family, a person to be respected and cared for. How she wanted to be such a mother, with Mari at her side to comfort her in times of trouble.

How secure her future seemed.

There was a shattering noise of gunfire outside the hut. The baby screamed, tears rolling down his hot face. Ana held him close, her eyes tight shut, trying to imagine herself somewhere else, far away, anywhere but there. She wished mammy were there instead of outside, where the guns were. Ana hated the guns.

Six months ago, all had seemed fine. They had sometimes been without food, but life had been peaceful in the village. Then, white men came, in a car, with big wheels. They brought the guns. At first only a few men had them, most thought that they were instruments of Satan, and would not touch them. Guns, however, began to mean power for those that held them. If a man did not give you what you wanted, you shot him. In the end, every man in her village and in those near it had a gun, even if it were just for self-defence. Some boys, Mari's age, and younger, had guns, looted from dead bodies or picked up from the ground after a fight. Ana hated it, for the simplest street brawl turned into a funeral. Ana's father had been shot only a few months ago over a piece of bread!

Ana hugged her brother tightly, as though keeping him close made up for the loss of her father.

"Pappy's with the angels now," she said, the tears welling up in her eyes. "He's safe now."

She wished everything were back to normal, before the guns had come.

Mari hid behind the tree near the old school gates. It was now a feeding station for the villages within fifty miles of the school. The choking fumes of lorries filled the yard, whilst the sounds of desperate mothers and screaming babies dominated the air.

Mari stood, frozen against the trunk of the tree, the low branches hiding him from view. Soon it would be time for him to strike. He fired two loud shots into the air, which rang around the vast yard. There was confusion. People ran in all directions, children wailed and mothers clung on to them, desperate not to lose them in the pandemonium which Mari had caused. Mari headed for the truck, climbed onto the metal platform, grabbed as much food as he could carry, jumped down, and made for home. This, he thought, was for Ana.

"How could you?" Ana screamed. "A gun? But you promised, you said you wouldn't!"

"But Ana, look what I've got, food." His voice was desperate.

"You didn't have to kill for it."

"I didn't! Just shot in the air."

Ana paused; she still didn't like it; this had happened before, with father. It always ended in tears, she knew.

"Please take it," he pleaded. "For me?"

She stretched out her hand, awkwardly. "All right, but no more, please!"

"OK." He handed her the grain, kissing her gently on the cheek. She felt a warm feeling burn inside her and smiled. "I love you Mari." He squeezed her hand.

"Me too."

Mari burst into the hut, flustered and excited.

"Ana! Ana!" he shouted. "I'm a soldier! Look, I've even got boots!"

Ana's heart sank to her feet. "But won't you have to . . . to kill people?"

He stood still, pausing. "I suppose . . . I could try and miss them, if you like."

"I suppose you've got your own gun then."

"Yes, isn't it beautiful? See, brand new, made in the UK."

Ana took the cold, metal gun in her hands; it sent a shiver up her spine, and somehow, she couldn't look at it. The gun seemed evil, like it had some dark power within it, a power that had taken over Mari, the power that held a promise of food, clothes and shiny black boots. She looked over at Mari's beaming face and smiled weakly. Nothing would change his mind now, not when the power of the gun had got a hold of him.

"You know I don't like it," she said, handing him back the gun. His face fell.

"I've got to go away now though," he said, "to raid, in the mountains."

This was even worse for Ana. Was she going to lose him so soon? He could be killed far away somewhere, with no family or friends near him, she would never know. A tear rolled down Ana's cheek. "Are you really sure," she asked, "about being a soldier?"

"Yes," he replied. "Please wish me luck Ana."

She looked into his pleading eyes. "You'll need it," she said, and kissed him on the cheek. It seemed cold and hard, unlike the warm Mari she had always known.

"I'll never forget you Mari," she whispered.

"Don't say it like that," he said. "I'll be back soon."

He walked out of the hut, tall and stiff, like he'd changed, by just saying goodbye.

Ana watched him walk with the other boys into the dying sun behind the village, towards the mountains.

Danny Manning (12)

*Shipwrecked on the Skeleton Coast

The water lapped across his legs, lifting them off the sand,
then gently lowering them back. His skin was burnt raw and
his hair white with salt. The sun beat down on his bare face.

Slowly his eyes opened, revealing to him a bluish blur. After some minutes he became aware of the water at his feet, the throbbing in his head and the crashing sound of the surf not far away.

The blue blur turned into a cloudless sky with a glaring sun in the centre. He rolled over onto his front and then stood up, almost falling over on his face as the pain in his head increased violently. Instead he sat down on the hot sand

Danny Manning (12)

and closed his eyes. Even with his eyes shut, the brightness still seemed to penetrate, blurring his memory.

All he could remember was the booming sea all around him and the panic running through him. He got up again. Behind him, the beach rose into a towering dune and in front the surf rose and fell in a foaming rage.

He stared blankly at a piece of painted wood being thrown about in the waves. As his eyes drifted along the shore he noticed more wreckage, bits of wood, net and a broken beer bottle.

He looked down at his bare feet, but more at the firm sand beneath them.

A sudden surge of joy overcame the agony. He felt safe now, knowing that his willpower had been rewarded after all those hours in the water, hoping that land was near.

Then his thoughts turned to other things. Where was everybody? If he had survived, surely they must be somewhere?

In both directions the beach stretched to the horizon, leaving watery images on the sand. He called out, but his own voice sounded so small in the face of the sea and the dunes. He listened so intently that he almost thought he heard a reply.

But the beach was empty. There was no trace of human life, or any other, apart from his own. He felt like the last person alive. Perhaps he was. The vast nothingness scared him. As his lips dried from the sea water, they split and a trickle of blood dribbled down his chin and dripped onto the sand below him.

Perhaps the others had already gone and left him behind. A new panic surged in him. He had to see over the sand dunes. There must be a road or a house, *somewhere*.

He began a stumbling run towards the dunes. Lights flashed in front of his face as he hit the ground. He lifted his head. His breathing was heavy and tears were running down his face.

In a frenzy he got up and started running again. As he ran further and further from the sea, his feet began to sink deeper into the soft, hot sand. He half crawled, half ran up the dune, desperately trying to reach the top. Again and again he slid back down on his stomach, his mouth covered with sand. At last one hand broke the knife edge at the top of the dune, and he wrenched himself up the last few feet.

What he saw made him cry out in horror and despair.

Endless waves of sand reached out in front of him to the edge of the world. He wept. Great sobs burst out from him, shaking him violently and his tears fell into the dry sand of the Namib desert.

He lay there for what seemed like hours, terrified of the sand, the dunes, the emptiness, the loneliness.

Eventually he stood up and in a frantic run, as if not to be left behind, he toppled down the other side of the dune. At the bottom he staggered to his feet and for a while the panic drove him. Then, as he clambered up yet another dune, he slowly became aware of a whistling howl.

He watched the sharply defined line at the top of the dune being whisked into a swirling haze. In a few moments the sand was lashing against his skin. What had previously appeared solid seemed to become part of the air. The sand blew out from underneath his feet and whipped up against his legs.

For a moment he remembered and felt again that day, thousands of miles away, when as a boy he had walked out onto a frozen lake at home. The ice suddenly collapsed beneath him, plunging him into the freezing water. His father's hands had wrenched him out to safety.

But here there was only sand and heat. And there was no one to pull him out.

He collapsed to his knees. His eyes blurred and everything spun around him. He couldn't think where he was or what he was doing. In one last desperate effort he lifted his head.

The storm swirled the sand into hundreds of different shapes and patterns. "But what was that?" he thought to himself. Two figures appeared walking through the sandy mist towards him. As they approached they seemed to fade and appear again erratically.

"They've come back for me!" he mumbled to himself. "At last!" He lay down backwards, exhausted and relieved.

They seemed now to be walking through the air. Just in front of him they stopped and a familiar pair of hands reached down to him, the same that had pulled him free from the ice.

He smiled and shut his eyes. He was safe now. He could let go.

The sand began to drift over and cover him. In a few minutes the desert was empty again.

Alicia Rix (12)

African Sun

The African sun was like an angry swirl of molten lava, crested with bruised purple. Even the jagged silhouettes of the skulking palm trees could not mask its fiery appearance as it beat relentlessly down on the dry, barren landscape of the African bush. But even the majestic tyrant of the sky could not banish out life. For it was plain for anyone to see or hear that the bush was alive.

It was alive with every hissing cicada and leathery necked chameleon. It was alive with every heart beat of the strong, lithe lion cubs, tawny-furred and black-eyed, and with every hoof beat of the restless zebras which, unique with their striped and glistening hides, pranced nervously to and fro, warily swishing their tails, nuzzling each other.

And so it could certainly not be said that life in the wilds of Africa was dull. The merest suggestion was ridiculous. But when the sun was pouring down its rays as strongly as it was that day, after a fortnight of drought, then it can safely be said that the people of Kenya carried heavy hearts beneath their beautiful, white smiles, and did not, perhaps, laugh as freely as before. For everyone knew what a drought in Africa was like. It meant blisters, cracking lips, poor crops and parched throats. It meant forest fires, disagreement, people desperate for water, for soaking, drenching, cold, relief. It meant thirst.

And sure enough, these were the very thoughts plaguing the minds of the people living in the small village, Baskhir, of the bush. For the moment there was water from the nearby waterhole. But the animals needed water also, and were beginning to get aggressive, and the water was drying quickly,

81

sucked up by the heat, the exhausting heat of the strenuous day.

Only one, the only one, perhaps of the village that did not feel so keenly the lack of water had the strength to get up that day to go to the waterhole in search for water. Karri Kaal, the youngest and most spirited member of the small community still held her head high, walking with pride, with her stubby little plaits swinging defiantly out behind her. She was tall for her age and her skin was a dark, luscious, treacle brown. On her face one wicked little scar remained from when she had valiantly tried to rear a stranded, feral cat. It had taken her a long time to tame it, and she had won many scratches from it too. But once Karri Kaal had got her mind on something she would stick to it and stick she did. The whole village was astonished to see her walking primly down the mud rutted path with the cat trailing meekly after her, as docile as a kitten.

Perhaps Karri felt the heat, but admit it she would not. Her pride was as strong as the sun in the sky, nay stronger, and though little beads of sweat appeared on her forehead as with everyone else, she would ignore them, and her dark eyes would flash with contempt at the idea of fretting because the sun was hot.

And then the sickness struck and people died. There were no ice packs to cool fevered brows, nor soothe delirious minds. The people were helpless, and the people kept on dying. Many old people died, and many young people died. Karri Kaal's Grandmother did not die. Like her granddaughter she would not accept defeat and she sat in the little mud hut and smoked her pipe, and made smoke rings wreathe around the room, muttering to herself as she watched them float and contort in the steaming air. She was eighty-five and looked older, and felt younger. She knew what would have to be done in the case of the drought, and when things became desperate she knew that her plan would have to take action whether she liked it or not. For, truth to tell, it was not a pleasant nor easy task, and she had pondered over it for days, wondering when the time would come. She realised it had come now and called Karri to her, into the mysterious depths of the hut which was dark, stuffy and smelt strongly of tobacco and which Karri liked for its privacy.

"Karri, no water has come yet, the people are thirsty and the waterhole is dry. Someone will have to go in search for new water."

Karri watched her Grandmother, and the smoke rings that floated and fluttered round the dark room, and she listened silently. Her Grandmother watched her carefully and knowingly in the dark.

"Someone must go. Will it be Paddy? I will call him now," said Karri Kaal's Grandmother, still watching, and yet making no move. Then Karri Kaal spoke, she said:

"I will go Grandmother," and lifted her head high in the air and Karri Kaal's Grandmother smiled and nodded her head to herself in the gloom and said quietly, "I know you shall, of course. Who else would it be when all the village is sick?" And then she turned her back and Karri went out of the hut.

She left in the evening, soundlessly making her way out of the village. And she was glad for the cooler night, and the purple sky which enveloped her in its velvety shawl and covered her from the world. When she felt her bare feet hit the sand she knew she had left the village behind. She felt strangely alone, and yet not alone at all. Her body was filled with some exclusive exaltedness which only she alone could feel and her heart thrilled and danced and sang and her eyes shone as she sprinted through the thick, soft, silky gold all around her, and looked towards the barren land she was about to enter. There were few trees and a few clumps of stiff, thick grass. She found the place beautiful in a rough, rugged way. It was so untouched by the human hand. Nature had woven its spell here. She was not a human. She was another creature of the wild. She belonged here and she felt it keenly in her heart which swelled as she hurried to begin her quest before dawn.

She travelled all night. Sometimes stumbling, sometimes crying out silently as her feet caught on sharp rocks and her hair became entangled in thick thorn trees and bushes. She could hear the Hartebeests snorting and the buffaloes stamping at the hard, dry earth, raking up clods of stiffened mud and clay. She finally fell asleep, exhausted on a broken tree stump, her head pillowed on a pile of dead leaves and her feet curled up beneath her. When dawn came with its exquisite, burning colours she awoke with a start and staggered to her feet before the sun arose properly and sought her out in the exposed, dry landscape. She ran, and her feet were sore and bruised. She picked the raw mangoes and tried to eat their unripe fruit, envying the giant hornbills which gorged themselves on the berries she knew she could not eat. And still Karri Kaal would not give up. Would not go back to the thirsty village, would not, ever, ever, ever, admit she'd failed. She would sooner die.

After some time however, she knew she could not go on without a rest and she stopped for a little while, squatting on the ground and making patterns in the clay similar to the one she had seen on the floors of the huts at home. She was clumsy and the twig felt alien in her hand but she enjoyed it thoroughly, only wishing she had some dyes to colour them red and blue and goldy orange. And then she heard the lioness roar. She heard her roar and for a moment she could not move. She began to shake violently and her eyes watered. Karri Kaal could look danger in the face. She could bravely battle through heat and drought and sickness but she could not fight the battle of the lioness and for the first time in her whole life Karri Kaal was afraid and she did not like the feeling. Her feet seemed rooted to the ground. She tried to mumble a prayer through her whitened lips. She forgot about water, she longed, no, more than longed for home and security. She could not die alone and yet she could not live, not against that kind of strength. She stood up and trembled but she thought calmly, to try and ease herself. At the back of her mind she could almost hear the silent footprints of the lioness but she forced herself to stay calm, because she remembered something her old Grandmother had taught her. Panic is that which a desperate man seeks, and you cannot live in panic, no more than you can live in a hurricane. Karri knew the words were true. The lioness roared again, closer this time and this time she ran. She ran blindly, leaping over low branches, over rocks and through thicket. She could feel the power pressing against her, could feel the fear and excitement streaming through her body, could see the world fly past her, the sweat running down her face, into her eyes. The lioness was running behind her, hungry for her food and for her cubs, hungry for the pleasure of killing, and only a few steps behind. Karri kept on running achingly through the dense bush, her hands were bleeding, how much longer could she last? And then came her chance. A fallen branch coated in dry brittle leaves blocked her way. There was just room for her to squeeze in amongst the twigs and leaves, covered by a blanket of crackling vegetation. She shut her eyes as the lioness bounded forward and with a great leap cleared the branch under which Karri was hiding. She felt sick with relief.

For at least half an hour she crouched in her hiding place, shuddering at her near escape, weeping as she had never wept before. It was her only moment of weakness.

At last she crept out, still tremulous with fear but holding her head high, and continued her search. The days seemed much longer now and she struggled not to faint. The only liquid she got was from fruit, often rotten or half eaten by monkeys, so desperate was her want. The soles of her feet were blistered and callused and had hardened along her journey and toughened, so that she hardly felt the hard ground now, nor the stones that had stung her feet before. She kept on, sometimes wearily. She had no idea of time. It was just heat, heat and more heat before the blessed night came. And the great, gold, honey-coloured moon, catching the last rosy rays of the departing sun gazed sympathetically down at her, as if reading her thoughts.

And then the days turned to weeks and she found herself thinking less about the village which was just a hazy memory and more about staying alive. Though it was true that occasionally her thoughts would stray to her Grandmother and she wondered if they would all be still waiting patiently, or had given up hope. But she knew in her secret soul that her Grandmother would never give up hope, ever.

She promised herself she would find water. She promised herself with a heart that tried to believe her promise and a courage to be proud of. Sometimes it looked as if the bush would never end. Perhaps there was no end, or no water. The thought was so horrible that she checked herself and carried on boldly.

She was growing thinner, noticeably. Not that there was anyone to notice her. Her hair was thicker though, and longer though very tangly and matted, and of a ripe and glossy sheen bleached slightly lighter by the sun. Amazingly she was getting used to the heat. It still scorched her with rays of violent heat, but it was endurable, she could tolerate it now. Sometimes she dreamed of water. Of pure, blue glistening water, for ever and for ever. And in her dreams she cried out for it, with cracked and bleeding lips and the animals were the only ones to hear her.

And then it happened. The sign she had been waiting for. It happened one day as she was walking through the undergrowth and she noticed it was not so hot. Surprised, she ran on and something wet and slimy clung to her foot, she screamed.

It was not a real scream of revulsion. It was the fact that the thing was moist, wet. She was unused to the touch, and tears came to her eyes. Looking down she saw a small green frog and a little quirk of excitement shot through her. Frogs needed water, frogs lived by water . . . She began, uncertainly to run and then to sprint through the bush not caring what stood in her way as she wheeled fast round a large clump of bushes and stopped dead. Stopped and stared. Blinked. Rubbed her eyes, then opened them. Stared. There was a big blue lake in front of her. Big and sapphire blue. Glistening wet in the sunlight, smiling at her. She gave a gasp and ran forward, and threw herself in, closing her eyes in ecstasy as the water enveloped her, splashing it over herself again and again and again. Taking great gulps, feeling the strength seep through her muscles. She came to the surface and was about to dive in again when to her astonishment she heard people talking. They were foreign, certainly, for she did not know their language. Curiously she looked up. Two men, in green uniform with caps on were talking and laughing. When they caught her glance they stopped. The first man walked forward tentatively, extending his hand. Karri crawled out blissfully and looked at him in surprise. The man smiled. "Jambo?" he said nervously, which is Kenyan for "Hello" and then, in excellent African, "Could you tell me where we are? We're rather stuck!"

Wiping her face Karri explained that the nearest village

was miles away but as she was going back there herself (Oh joy!) she could guide them. Briefly she told them about the drought and gestured that they take water back, to which they agreed enthusiastically, smiling and dipping flasks into the lake, filling them to the brim. Karri watched greedily, her heart felt as free as a bird. And as she journeyed back with the two men she told them of everything that had passed, as best she could, and everything which you have just finished reading. The tale of what one determined girl could do.

Katie-Ellen McCrory (11)

*Lone Star

One night
As I went to bed
I left my window open.
A star dropped into my room
And cowered in a corner
Trying to warm itself by the radiator.

I hoped it would not be caught
By the moon
And sent back
To solitary confinement
In the night.

It told me
It was lonely.

I cry in my dark cell
A prisoner of an awful crime.
I stole the sun
And was banished.
My life sentence
Began before time.

I am cold
You cannot warm me
I am ice
You cannot thaw me
I am ash
You cannot touch me
Or I crumble to dust.

I woke to the ticking of my clock.
My room was still and cold.
There was a smell,
Like a bonfire which had burned out
Years ago.
The fat sun
Squeezed through my window
Throwing the shadows around my room
Searching for something.

In the corner,
A puddle
In place of my star.

UNRAVELLING A THREAD
OF HISTORY

Elizabeth Leeds (14)

Jessica Welsh (12)

*Young Planets

She stared at the signs and notice boards, the people talking in the street below her. The shape of the letters seemed strange, foreign. Their alphabet was a peculiar one, she thought. It sounded so . . . she paused for a moment . . . illogical. And the words seemed almost random in their spelling. As for their pronunciation, well, it made her wince to think how mangled and distorted it had become.

But what annoyed her most of all was the way they lived their lives. So sloppy and haphazard. Mixing comedy and tragedy into a strange kind of bitter-sweet cocktail. It was most undignified.

But that was what she had come to expect from these young planets. Chaos and disorder. They had no idea of organisation. No one knew what to say or when to say it. They seemed to trust everything to Mother Nature.

She pondered for a moment on the strange old-fashioned name they had given her. So trusting, so naive. Looking upon her as a kind of minor Deity. She realised that they had no idea, even of what she was.

Yet in a way, it was flattering to be so indispensable. Many of the other worlds had tried to do away with her a long time ago. They had their technology, their super-computer thingies. What did they need an old, old woman for? But even the more advanced worlds had not quite grasped the concept of her. What she was and what she could do. They still thought that they controlled her with their silly games, that they could just flick her away like an unbent paperclip. Well it didn't work like that.

And now this place. This "Earth". It had started off so

well. Such a neat little sphere of green and blue. So self-contained, so sheltered. Her favourite plant. And she had tended it carefully, watching it develop and grow. And then she turned her back for one moment. And all of a sudden she found that her precious world had blossomed into a weed.

Too much control, that was the problem. She had given them too much control. She should not have let them discover fire. That had been the vital mistake. But to take it back now would be too, too dangerous. It would mean unravelling a thread of history. They had grown too used to being on top of everything, they had grown complacent. And now, this poisoned seed had been flung into their midst. Someone, someone had given them ... weapons.

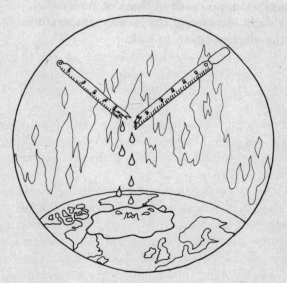

"Just a slight increase of the Earth's temperature .... And the glaciers began to melt."

Rachel Bowden (13)

She grit her teeth in anger. Her favourite world had been deliberately sabotaged. It was too late for her to do anything about it now. Now Earth would be blown apart from the inside, shattered by war and discontent.

And she would have to watch it suffer, slowly dwindle into insignificance, or turn into another desert – barren of life.

She had tried to create a solar system. An organised network of planets, self-contained.

But now she was tired of her game. Someone had spoilt it for her.

And her toy. She felt an obligation to put it out of its misery.

She pointed at the tiny sphere, and turned her head.

No explosion, no crash of thunder, no smoke.

Just a slight increase of the Earth's temperature.

And the glaciers began to melt.

Judith Rideout (16)

*The Oppression of a Liberated Sister in the Year 2058

What was I doing twenty years ago tonight, the twentieth anniversary of the Gynorevolution? I remember being with one of those creatures called men. It was oppressing me, exploiting my sex. I was on a "date" with it. Big Sister says that we were phallocentrically socially conditioned into dating by the male creatures – it allowed them to retain physical, economical and emotional access to us. Their dominance in the former tyranny depended on our heterosexuality, our willingness to submit ourselves to them. They did this through dating, marriage and the nuclear family. Big Sister says that we were so oppressed we were seduced by their lies and we believed that they loved us. Thanking Diana, the LesboFeminist movement ended the deception.

It was this night, twenty years ago, that the hardcore LF freedom fighters used their superior military strategy and strength to conquer the phallocratic government; the government's army was massacred before they realised what was happening. Don't worry young femdels,* they were only men – the LesboFeminist state is not a cruel one. The LF then secured her power using hard-right policies and, of course, by creating overnight a femdelic police state. All men were disempowered and confined to various ghettos. Any troublemakers were shot. The LF also destroyed the huge,

---

*Although most words in Femspeak are merely adaptations of prerevolutionary words, some, such as woman (femdel, adj. femdelic) are unrecognisable in order to remove any association with men. The word LesboFeminist remains unchanged, however, because it was coined before the Revolution and serves to remind femdels of The Struggle.

misguided, patriarchal institution that was the Christian Church so that femdels would no longer have to worship the vengeful, misogynist God that we worshipped during the great Oppression. Now we worship the mother goddess Diana, the personification of everything femdelic; nature and gentleness are examples of this. Diana is also the antithesis of all things masculine. Remember young femdels, that violence, hate, greed, war and destruction are also masculine traits, and they should not be found in you when you grow up.

I can't quite remember the date when all men were officially deported to Manterritory, but it will be in your hystery books. Manterritory was the land designated for all phallus bearers. On this land were built houses, painted black, to show femdels that they should not enter, for black is the colour of evil, violence and corruption, is it not?

The men creatures, stripped of all their possessions and external weaponry, entered their new community with reluctance, and there was much trouble. However, when the LF police installed lager taps into every house there was no more trouble, for the subhuman half of our species used these taps every night and this caused them to start killing or maiming each other in their alcoholic stupor, thus they deflected their anger from us. The alcohol also made them too ill to fight, too ill to think even, although any femdel worth her oestrogen knows that male thinking, poisoned with primitive testosterone, is far inferior to ours. Because of this, young femdels, *men* do *men*ial tasks because it befits them, although men with exemplary genetic material may supplement their income by donating to an LF sperm bank, situated on the territorial borders. The men donating now are contributing to the F3 generation of LesboFeminists – you, my young femdels, are the F2 generation.

However, you will undoubtedly be aware of current pioneering techniques in fusing together two ova to form a

George Robusti (16)

viable, and always femdelic zygote. Soon the male involvement in reproduction can be phased out, and the evil Y chromosome will vanish for ever. Isn't that a wonderful thought?

To return to the lesson. We could now, with our bullies resituated, begin the process of body decolonisation; we were physically efemcipated from the rapists of our species and could now take part in natural relationships where each partner is equal and neither in fear. Heterosexuality, the sick perversion of twisted and deprived minds was and is, quite rightly, banned, for not only is it a moral abomination but a danger to femdels and the LF. Consider this – if men brutally penetrate femdels, they will brutally penetrate the Femterritory and could perhaps destroy the LF. Consequently, and remember this, any non-Policesister caught talking to a man will be imprisoned for five years. Also, and this is of grave importance, any femdel caught in mid-coitus with a man will be sent to Womb 101, a special terrifying place where she will be taught the cruel fate that her foremothers underwent in male hands. Then she is indoctrinated with the Diana texts and made to repent.

You may be wondering, young femdels, where all of this is leading. I will tell you a story now that will shock you. It is my ovarimony of shame.

I once fell in love (or so I thought) with a man, and I did do disgusting unnatural acts with him, even with the full knowledge that the pure, clean method of baby-making is to go to a sperm bank. Please excuse me for crying when I remember what I did, how I spat in the face of my liberators by sneaking past the checkpoints between the territories, and going to the house of a male creature. It was of good genetic material and consequently it had furniture in its house, although it wore the compulsory purple overalls that men must wear to prevent mistaken gender identity. It must have earned a lot of Gynocredits from selling its sperm because it showed me contraband that it had managed to obtain – old books from a long time before the revolution. I pray that you never have the misfortune to be corrupted by men and ideas from books like I was. One book, dating from some forty years before the revolution, was called – if I remember correctly – "The Joy of Sex". On reading it, I saw a word which I had never seen before, and I asked the male to explain it to me. It said that the word could not be explained using other words, but for me to understand fully what the word meant, I would have to experience it, using the male's body. On my shameful discovery, I embarked on a catalogue of sin, which I will not expand on since I would prefer your minds innocent of my evil. I was finally caught back in Femterritory, after being overheard by the secret LF police, talking of this new word, the "o" word, to a friend of mine. They knew that the word had come from Manterritory and realised my experiences. Thus was I rushed to Womb 101, to be informed that the "o" word was a heretical word, not to be found in the official lexicon. I had not known this. Please do not ask me what the word is as I would sooner die before telling you. The LF so fear the "o" word because it could be the key to the male repossession of power and therefore to enlighten your sisters of the "o" word is, young femdels, the greatest crime against your gender that you can perpetrate.

So there was I, incarcerated in Womb 101, for the two greatest crimes – heterosexual love and utterance of the "o" word. At the time I remember feeling anger and frustration at my imprisonment, at being separated from the person I loved, for doing what I thought was natural. Now, however, I know the truth. Those wonderful sisters of mine – and yours – showed me my wrong-doing, brought about by my ignorance. Every day I rejoice in Diana's temple for my illuminating sojourn in Womb 101.

For now I realise that, contrary to my former belief, it is impossible for me to have greatly enjoyed my physical experiences with a man and for me to have loved a man – it had used its dominant character to induce me into a state of false consciousness, that is, it brainwashed me into believing in our mutual love. Indeed, Big Sister has shown me that men are incapable of love and I want to pass on my knowledge to my sisters. Through my experiences of a man, I can now teach you, the young femdels, you who were born after the Revolution, about just how evil men really are. Hopefully then I can try to forget my folly, comforted in the knowledge that others have learned from my mistakes, and pray that, in time, Diana will forgive me.

Aaron Jarman (12)

*My Godmother's Wedding

The bride and groom dance.
Her dress, an up-turned lily flower,
Spins like a whirlpool of soft white water.
He, like a black spectre
Encompassing the lily,
Moves her through the crowd
As lightly as a thought.
The room is filled with voices,
The drone interwoven with heavy laughter,
Creating a complex tapestry of sound.
Guests' features are blurred and tempered
By the misty green.
Two families blend into one.
United strangers exchange well worn stories and fixed
smiles.
Silence descends on the feast,
And all eyes turn to the cake,
An architectural structure of planes and pillars,
Supporting an avalanche of pink and white icing.
The lily and the spectre lift the knife
To cut the silence, to slice the avalanche.
Cheers and sounds of crystal on crystal
Toast the union of the bride and groom.

Funkerella
(Or, A Tale of A Modern Princess)

(Funkerella is sitting in the kitchen. She can be either playing on a hand-held game or reading a book. Her mother, Marian, enters, carrying a sheaf of papers bound with a red ribbon. The papers are marked "Divorce".)

Marian: Ah, Funkerella.

Funkerella: What is it, Mum?

Marian: I've just come in to say that I'm divorcing your father . . .

Funkerella: What?!

Marian: And I'm off to LA to have the time of my life.

Funkerella: Cool! When do we start packing?

Marian: Sorry dear, your father won custody. *(sweeps out)* Goodbye.

(Salmonella enters, with Pneumonia and Listeria close behind her.)

Salmonella: Good morning, Funkerella.

Funkerella: Good morning, erm, ah, who are you?

Salmonella: Less of your cheek, girl.

Funkerella: But who are you?

Salmonella: I am the Lady Salmonella, now wife of the Baron Boring.

Funkerella: The Baron Boring? But he's my *father*!

Salmonella: *And* my husband.

Funkerella: You mean? . . .

Salmonella: Yes, I do. I'm your stepmother. And, of course, my two girls, Pneumonia and Listeria, are children of my own blood and thus vastly superior to *you*.

Funkerella: That's not fair!

Salmonella: But it is fair by my rules. And my rules rule here. Don't they, Listeria?

Listeria: Of course, Mater.

Salmonella: And talking of "Mater" . . .

Funkerella: Were we?

Salmonella: My two daughters call me Mater, and I shall expect the same degree of respect from you, even though you are not my daughter.

Funkerella: No way!

Salmonella: Less of your cheek. And what is your name?

Funkerella: Funkerella.

Salmonella: Who gave you that name?

Funkerella: My father.

Salmonella: There *are* some things he does which I simply can't abide. But now, whatever-your-name-is (I am not calling you Funkerella) you can get on with cleaning the house and doing all the other menial tasks whilst I and my children go upstairs to watch Neighbours. *(hands Funkerella a bottle)* And here's the Fairy Liquid.

Funkerella: But Mum!

Salmonella: No buts. And I'm not your mother. *(exits)*

Funkerella: But slavery's illegal! Under the Universal Declaration of Human Rights!

Salmonella: I said, *no buts*.

Funkerella: *(in desperation)* Article 4!

(It is a few days later, in the palace of the Principality of X. Queen Xanthe and King Xavier are sitting on their thrones. Prince Groovy is standing in front of them.)

Groovy: Look, Mum, I really can't marry any of the soppy little princesses you've brought in from far and wide. They're just not my type! One of them was *nine years old*!

Xanthe: We were planning for the future.

Groovy: That's as it may be. But I simply couldn't marry her, anyway.

Xavier: I didn't see anything wrong with her.

Groovy: No, you couldn't. You're her godparent, for heaven's sake!

Xanthe: That's as it may be. But we still have to find you a bride before you're twenty-one-and-a-half or the principality goes to your cousin over in Australia.

Groovy: No! He still thinks *Kylie Minogue* is brilliant!

Xavier: I thought that would get him moving.

Groovy: But anyway, we've still got *lots* of time.

Xanthe: We most certainly have *not*. You were twenty-one *yesterday*.

Groovy: Um.

Xavier: I don't see what was wrong with that girl you rescued from that hundred-year sleep.

Groovy: *I* do! She thought *Mr Blobby* was still *Number One*!

Xanthe: The question still remains, how do we find you a bride?

Groovy: We could try Dateline . . .

Xavier: Most certainly not!

Groovy: Or there's always the Lonely Hearts . . . "Attractive young prince, 21, with money, seeks woman to be his bride, must be up to date with current music scene" . . .

Xanthe: I forbid you *now* to put an advertisement in the Lonely Hearts . . . What *are* the Lonely Hearts, Xavier?

Xavier: Advertisements in newspapers, Xanthe dear . . .

Xanthe: I *still* forbid you to put an advertisement in one, Groovy.

Groovy: Or how about the Valentine's Messages?

Xavier: There will be *no* Valentine's Messages.

Groovy: All right, I can see your minds are made up . . . I'm going to go to my room, and *please*! *No more* of this bride nonsense! Why do I *have* to marry, anyway?

Xanthe: *(holds up scroll, this can simply be Marian's divorce papers turned the other way round)* It's the law.

Xavier: And you're going to follow it, because you're *my* son and you do what *I* tell you.

Groovy: For heaven's sake! The age of majority's *eighteen*!

Xanthe: It may be in the rest of the country, but in X it's twenty-five.

Groovy: OK, but just leave me alone and let me think!

(Again, it is a few days later and we are in the Principality of X, where the throne room is arranged as in the last scene. Groovy is reading a magazine; "Smash Hits" or anything else appropriate. Xanthe and Xavier enter, and take their seats.)

Xavier: Ah, Groovy. Have you made up your mind yet?

Groovy: About what?

Xanthe: About who is to be your future bride.

Groovy: Not that again.

Xavier: Do you really want the crown to go to your cousin?

Xanthe: He's already married, you know. To Princess Pyracanthus. She was on our shortlist for you, until your cousin snapped her up.

(Xavier is leafing through Groovy's magazine; he looks up.)

Xavier: You know, Xanthe dearest, I've had an idea about how we can choose Groovy's bride.

Xanthe: Yes, darling? How?

Xavier: This magazine of Groovy's gave me the idea. Why don't we hold a disco?

Xanthe: A what?

Xavier: A disco, Xanthe dearest. You know. One of those things with coloured music and loud lights where lots of people bop about all night.

Xanthe: I don't quite understand. Is it one of those things

Groovy likes so much?

Xavier: Yes, Xanthe dearest.

Xanthe: A brilliant idea! Call the Royal Register!

Xavier: Royal *Registrar*, Xanthe dearest.

Xanthe: Whatever. Have him comb through the birth records of the land! And have the Royal Listmaker collate all those of women between sixteen and forty! And have the Royal Mail send out to all of those women invitations to the Prince's Disco!

Xavier: The Royal Registrar's a woman now. Equal Opportunities.

Groovy: *Forty*! Make it twenty-five!

Xanthe: Don't argue with your parents, Groovy dear. Forty it shall be. There *is* such a thing as ageism now.

Groovy: I know, I know.

Xavier: So a disco it is, then?

Groovy: Yes.

Xanthe: And, of course, if you do not find your future bride there, we, as your parents, will use our right to choose a bride for you.

Groovy: But *Mum*!

Xavier: Don't "But Mum!" us. A Bride-Choosing Disco it shall be.

Xanthe: Call the Royal Register!

Xavier: Royal *Registrar*, darling . . .

(It is ten days later, and Funkerella is clearing up the remains of breakfast. Pneumonia is waiting for the post. Seven letters flop through the door.)

Pneumonia: Three bills for the Baron . . . something for you, Mum . . . something for me . . . this is for you, Listeria . . . and one for you, Funkerella.

(Salmonella, Pneumonia, Listeria and Funkerella each open their letters.)

Pneumonia: Wow! A letter from the *Prince*!

Salmonella: What does it say? *(sarcastically)* Dear Squidgy?

Pneumonia: Nothing like that, Mum. It's an invite to his disco. He wants to choose a future bride!

Listeria: You got ambitions then? *(pulls her letter out of its envelope)* Mine says that too! I'm more beautiful than you . . . bet he'll marry *me*!

(Boring comes downstairs)

Boring: Ah, morning, you lot . . . *(Pneumonia hands him his letters)* Water, electricity . . . you been leaving lights on again? . . . Red notice on the phone bill, well, I can't afford to pay it yet, I'm worse off than the landless knights . . . they'll have to disconnect it, and you'll have to write to all your friends, Listeria . . . what are you bickering about?

Pneumonia: We've got invites to the Prince's disco! We could be his *bride*!

Boring: Oh yes, there are already odds on who he's going to marry down at the bookie's . . . wasn't there something for Funkerella?

Listeria: Yes, she's taken it.

Funkerella: *(from the kitchen)* Wow!

Pneumonia: We can all guess what she's got.

Funkerella: It's an invite to the Prince's disco!

Listeria: I thought so. *(goes into kitchen)* Well, she's not going to be competition for *us*.

(Funkerella shrieks; there is a ripping sound)

Pneumonia: What did you do?

Listeria: I ripped it into shreds and put it down the waste disposal.

Pneumonia: Very good, don't you think, Mum?

Salmonella: Yes. We don't want her running around spoiling *our* chances of getting in with the Prince.

Listeria: So you're going then, Mum?

Salmonella: Well, of course! I've been invited (I'm only

thirty-nine), and you'll need a chaperone. There might be muggers or rapists.

Pneumonia: The Prince wouldn't invite them!

Salmonella: They could sneak in. And *my* word is final, because you're in *my* house.

Funkerella: But what about me?

Salmonella: I should have thought it was obvious. You stay at home, look after the house, and clean up after us. We go to the disco, have no cares at all, dance our socks off and get in with a chance of marrying . . . the Prince!

Funkerella: But it's not fair!

Salmonella: It's fair by *me*.

(It is the night of the disco. Salmonella and her daughters are upstairs getting ready, forever calling Funkerella to help them.)

Listeria: Funkerella!

Funkerella: Yes?

Listeria: Find my green eyeshadow.

Funkerella: You haven't got any. You have purple.

Listeria: Well I like green better, so find some for me now.

Pneumonia: What green eyeshadow, Listeria? Mine's disappeared . . . in suspicious circumstances!

Listeria: You mean I tea-leafed it?

Pneumonia: Of course.

Listeria: Well, you little . . . that's not what I would expect from my own, full sister. I'd expect it from Funkerella, she hasn't got our mother's pure, honest blood in her . . . but you, Pneumonia!

Pneumonia: How can you say that about me?

Listeria: Very easily.

Pneumonia: There is such a thing as a law of slander, you know!

Listeria: Yes, and I plan to invoke it.

108

Pneumonia: It's I who should be invoking it . . . you slandered me.

Listeria: Then do you want the court to hear about what you said about me when Mater's purse went missing?

Pneumonia: Well . . .

Listeria: Funkerella!

Funkerella: Yes?

Listeria: Pass me the perfume.

Funkerella: Which one? There's a lot of bottles here . . . ah, this looks like the one . . . oh no! This one's labelled "hydrochloric acid, very corrosive" . . . I'll give you this one, it looks like Chanel. *(hands Listeria a bottle)*

Listeria: Thank you. Yes, this is the one, the Channel Tunnel Number 5.

Pneumonia: Funkerella!

Funkerella: Yes?

Pneumonia: Have you got my outfit ready yet?

Funkerella: Yeah, I'll just find where I put it.

Pneumonia: You mean you don't know where it is?

Funkerella: No.

Pneumonia: You little . . .

Funkerella: Don't worry, I left it on your bed.

Pneumonia: That's all right then. Do you like it, Listeria?

Listeria: Yeah, and I'm sure the Prince will too.

Pneumonia: Yeah. I'll be the one marrying him, you know.

Listeria: It'll be me. I'm much more beautiful than you are.

Pneumonia: That's not true!

Listeria: Oh yes, it is. He'll fall for my fragrant perfume immediately . . . my captivating green eyes . . .

Pneumonia: With *my* captivating green eyeshadow.

Listeria: That's enough from you.

Pneumonia: I'll go on as much as I want to. The only person who gets bossed about here is Funkerella.

Listeria: Well, of course.

Pneumonia: It's all her fault.

Listeria: Well, of course. Funkerella! Do my hair . . . this instant!

(Pneumonia, Listeria and Salmonella are leaving the house, leaving Funkerella alone for the night.)

Salmonella: Goodbye, Funkerella.

Funkerella: Bye, Salmonella. *(sniffs)*

Salmonella: Now I don't want any of that nasty snivelling, just because you haven't got an invitation to go to the disco.

Funkerella: But I did have an invitation!

Salmonella: Well, you haven't any more . . . thank you very much, Listeria.

Funkerella: But it wasn't fair! I got sent an invitation . . . the Prince wanted me to come!

Salmonella: Oh no, he didn't. Some people like me, and Pneumonia, and Listeria, are born to go to discos, and have chances of marrying Princes, and others, like you, Funkerella, are born to do work in the house, look after people who are born to higher things, and not to go to discos. In short, some people marry Princes, some people marry dustbin-men.

Pneumonia: And some people marry dustbins.

Listeria: Quite right, Pneumonia.

Salmonella: So shut up, Funkerella, and get back in the house. There's a list of things that you can do on the kitchen table.

(Salmonella et al. sweep away. Funkerella returns dejectedly into the house.)

Funkerella: It's not fair. I wish my real mum was back. Oh lord . . . I hope Dad's paying her maintenance like he's supposed to under the Child Support Act.

(Funkerella is sitting alone in the kitchen, complaining to herself.)

Funkerella: It isn't fair. She hasn't got a right to do this to me. I've been working for two whole months, ever since she came . . . I've got through forty bottles of Fairy. Joanna Lumley's advert seems to have influenced Salmonella a lot.

(*Funkerella picks up a bottle of Fairy, and wipes some washing-up liquid off it.*)

Funkerella: I wish I could have gone to the disco.

(*There is a puff of smoke off-stage, to the left. Funkerella picks up a water pistol, and turns to the left.*)

Funkerella: (*menacingly*) Don't move. I've got a gun.

(*Enter the Fairy Liquid, from the left.*)

Fairy Liquid: Are you Funkerella?

Funkerella: Yes.

Fairy Liquid: Thank goodness. I've come to the right place.

Funkerella: How do you mean? (*puts down water pistol*)

Fairy Liquid: A request was made, according to prescribed rules, and so it is my duty to call upon you and assist you in any way you feel necessary.

Funkella: What prescribed rules?

Fairy Liquid: (*holds up sheaf of papers, these can again be Marian's divorce papers turned the other way round*) The Laws of the Fairy Godmothers.

Funkerella: You mean you're my Fairy Godmother?

Fairy Liquid: Yes. (*grandiosely*) I am the Fairy Liquid!

Funkerella: Wow!

Fairy Liquid: And I am here to help you in any way I can.

Funkerella: But how did you get here?

Fairy Liquid: When you rubbed the Fairy bottle, I was instantly called up from Fairyland and despatched down to you. It's a bit like Group 4, except I don't escape on the way.

Funkerella: But what can you do for me?

Fairy Liquid: Your wish is my command!

Funkerella: What about world peace?

Fairy Liquid: I'm sorry, but I don't think I can run to that.

Funkerella: Oh well, then. Wait! I know what you can do for me!

Fairy Liquid: Good. I don't like being called out for no reason at all. And be careful what you rub in future. Now, what's your problem?

Funkerella: You see, my stepmother—

Fairy Liquid: I thought one of those might be in it somewhere.

Funkerella: —and her two daughters (she doesn't consider me her daughter, seeing as I haven't got her blood) have gone off to the Prince's disco, where he will choose his future bride.

Fairy Liquid: Which Prince is it? There's a lot round here.

Funkerella: It's Groovy.

Fairy Liquid: Oh yes, quite a cute one. I always thought he looked a bit like – oh dear, who? Never mind. Well, what do you want to do?

Funkerella: Go to the disco! What do you think I want to do?

Fairy Liquid: Right then. Let's be systematic about it. You need . . . transport. Very well. You wouldn't have a pumpkin here, by any chance?

Funkerella: Erm . . . I'm afraid not, but Salmonella uses cucumbers for her eyes.

Fairy Liquid: Well . . . It'll have to do, I suppose. Fetch it. *(Funkerella exits, and returns with large green cucumber.)*

Fairy Liquid: No, don't put it here! Even Supero-Carpet-Wax won't remove tyre stains.

Funkerella: Tyre stains?!

Fairy Liquid: Just you wait and see. Now take the cucumber outside and I'll see what I can magic up. *(leafs through large book)* Ah yes, this is the one, although it'll want changing so that it's up to date. Now, one, two, three . . .

112

(There is a puff of smoke to the right. Funkerella rushes to it.)

Funkerella: Wow, uh, Liquid! A Ferrari!

Fairy Liquid: I said the spell could do with some changing, didn't I?

Funkerella: It certainly did change.

Fairy Liquid: Now, what next?

Funkerella: I could do with a chauffeur to take me to the disco.

Fairy Liquid: Then a chauffeur it shall be. You wouldn't have a mouse on you, would you?

Funkerella: Well, not on me, no, but Pneumonia keeps some for her science class. She does things like feed them hydrochloric acid and see how they react.

Fairy Liquid: How barbaric. I think I shall report her to Against Animal Testing. Are there any which haven't drunk any acid yet?

Funkerella: There should be one. I'll fetch it. *(hurries offstage)*

Fairy Liquid: Put it inside the Ferrari on the driver's seat!

Funkerella: Why?

Fairy Liquid: You'll see!

(Fairy Liquid gestures with wand. There is another puff of smoke.)

Funkerella: Wow! A chauffeur!

Fairy Liquid: As requested. Oh heaven . . . what is it next?

Funkerella: I think some clothes might help. I can't really go to a disco looking like this.

Fairy Liquid: You're right. You can't. Now, let's see . . . you'll be wanting clothes, I take it, and shoes, and is make-up in fashion again now?

Funkerella: Yes.

Fairy Liquid: That gives me a sort-of-starting point. I'm

113

sorry I have to ask you all these questions, but I haven't done a job like this for two hundred years now.

Funkerella: Where do we start?

Fairy Liquid: I'd say with shoes, they're easiest. Pom pom pom . . . (*leafs through book*) Oh dear, I'm afraid I can only give you platforms, I've got the Nineteen Seventies Spell Supplement here. Platforms all right with you?

Funkerella: Certainly.

Fairy Liquid: And what's next?

Funkerella: Make-up, you said.

Fairy Liquid: Oh you're right, I did, I *am* a forgetful fairy. As I said, I haven't done anything like this for a few hundred years, so I'll need something to start you off with. Do your sisters wear make-up?

Funkerella: Yes, but it's all horrible colours.

Fairy Liquid: It doesn't matter. Just fetch it, and get into the other room.

(Funkerella does so. There is another puff of smoke.)

Funkerella: Brilliant, Liquid!

Fairy Liquid: Anything to oblige. Now you know where the car is. I must be off.

(Fairy Liquid starts to try to fly, but halts herself.)

Fairy Liquid: I nearly forgot! The spell wears off at midnight! Oh, when I go, I'll leave an alarm clock in the Ferrari! Now I really must be off! Goodbye!

Funkerella: *(from offstage)* Take me to the Palace!

(It is the Prince's disco, and guests are starting to arrive. Groovy is arguing with the DJ, Prince Pinnacle.)

Groovy: *Whitney Houston*?! Since when was she Number One?

Pinnacle: They were when I selected the records.

Groovy: Well you certainly aren't keeping up with the times! It's the Rednex who're Number One *now*!

Pinnacle: Nobody told me.

Groovy: You could have found out for yourself. I could do a better job myself!

Pinnacle: Then why don't you?

Groovy: Because I have to dance with my "future brides".

Pinnacle: Parents' idea, right?

Groovy: Uh huh.

(Xavier and Xanthe are arguing.)

Xanthe: God! Why are there all these princesses?! There's every one here except the ones from the Dominion of Domswergle!

Xavier: Why not Domswergle? I met their King at a conference, he seemed a nice chap.

Xanthe: You know we're not talking to them because of what they said about our Sharon.

Xavier: What *did* they say about our Sharon?

Xanthe: Too much.

Registrar: Presenting the Princesses Strepsil, Rennie, and Alka-Seltser!

Xavier: And whose idea was it to have the Royal Registrar announce each and every visitor?

Xanthe: Yours.

Xavier: Ah yes . . .

Registrar: The Princes Credence and Reliance!

Xanthe: I just hope he does choose a bride tonight.

Xavier: He'll find someone.

Registrar: The Princess Arcana!

Xanthe: Can't remember inviting *her*.

Xavier: You can't remember *anything*.

(Funkerella walks on to the dance floor, wearing the ensemble created by Fairy Liquid. Listeria and Groovy are dancing.)

Listeria: I'd like to get to know you better.

Groovy: Yes, that's very nice.

115

Listeria: I'll be open with you. I want to marry you.

(Groovy catches sight of Funkerella. He leaves Listeria, who is perturbed.)

Listeria: Come back, Princey-Wincey!

(Groovy walks over to Funkerella.)

Groovy: You must be the Princess Arcana.

Funkerella: Yes, I am.

Groovy: Where are you from?

Funkerella: This principality, actually. I'm on a gap year before university.

Groovy: That's brilliant.

Funkerella: Thank you.

Groovy: Would you like to dance? *(to Pinnacle)* This time I *want* Whitney Houston! *(to Funkerella)* You like Whitney Houston, don't you?

Funkerella: It's okay with me.

Groovy: That's all right. Anything to please.

Funkerella: I could dance with you for ever.

Groovy: Look, Arcana . . . I'd like to marry you.

(Funerella's alarm clock rings.)

Funkerella: I must go . . . my mother, the Queen Quirky, will freak out if I'm not back.

Groovy: You must come and see me again.

(Funkerella runs off, leaving behind one platform shoe. Groovy runs out after her, but Funkerella has gone. Only the shoe is left.)

Groovy: *(forlornly)* Who was she? All I know is that she comes from our principality? But she could live anywhere! I shall call out the Royal Registrar . . . she shall comb the principality until she finds the owner of this shoe. Oh, Arcana!

(It is a week later. The Registrar, holding the platform shoe, has knocked at Salmonella's door. Salmonella answers it.)

116

Salmonella: No, we do not want any encyclopaedias . . . Oh, hello, would you like a cup of tea?

Registrar: No thanks, I'm on an important mission for the Prince.

Salmonella: Ooh, what about, and why haven't I read about it in the Sun?

Registrar: Unlike mainland England, royal marital affairs are not leaked out to all and sundry.

Salmonella: Why are you here?

Registrar: I am on a mission to discover the owner of this platform shoe. *(holds out shoe)*

Salmonella: A shoe? Doesn't look like any of mine, but it could be Listeria's, she's always wearing strange things like that.

Registrar: So shall I come right in, and find out if any of your household is the Princess Arcana, who the Prince Groovy has vowed to marry? For he will be twenty-one-and-a-half tomorrow, but his bride must be found today!

Salmonella: Well I for one would love to marry a Prince.

Registrar: But only the Princess Arcana's foot will fit this platform shoe! So it is imperative that she is found!

Salmonella: Well come in then! *(she leads her through the door)*

Registrar: She'd better be here. This is the last house in the principality.

(Everyone, bar Funkerella, is in the living-room.)

Registrar: Pneumonia, come up and try this shoe.

Pneumonia: *(tries to put shoe on)* It fits!

Registrar: *(feels)* Oh no it doesn't. You're having to cram your foot in. Next!

Listeria: *(tries to put shoe on)* It fits *me*!

Registrar: *(feels)* Not you, either. This large toe gives you away. There must be another person in the house!

Salmonella: Well, there's Funkerella, but she wasn't at the disco.

Registrar: It's worth a try. Funkerella!

(Funkerella comes down.)

Funkerella: What is it?

Registrar: Could you try this shoe on, please?

(Funkerella does so. It fits.)

Registrar: So you are the Princess Arcana!

(Fairy Liquid appears.)

Fairy Liquid: Found your missing Princess at last?

Registrar: Phone Prince Groovy!

(She does so. Groovy comes in, through door.)

Groovy: So you are the Princess Arcana!

Funkerella: My name's Funkerella, actually.

Groovy: That name is even better! Oh, Funkerella!

Funkerella: Oh, Groovy!

Groovy: And shall tomorrow be our nuptial day?

(Xanthe and Xavier appear.)

Xanthe: Wonderful!

Xavier: So you have found a bride!

Groovy: Yes, and we wed tomorrow, among the June blossom.

Funkerella: Um, would the Bop-and-Hop Disco be better?

The Barons of Change

The new system. Monorail in the city, police keeping a tight watch on things. A man once said to me, "Cities are improving nowadays. I used to have to order Pizza on phone, but now, tap in a few numbers and it comes in seconds."

He was shot on October 11th in a slum bar, whilst talking with his friends.

I used to be a doctor. A good one. I had everything a doctor needed to have. But I thought too much and in those days, you weren't really meant to think.

There was a war going on, although no press ever touched it. It was the ground folk against Superon, the lord of my city. No one really knew about it as the ground folk never ventured into an ordinary man's life and the Lord never spoke about the war in public.

For a time, I lived in the place where we were meant to live, the middle class. Our job was to work, eat, sleep, have children and then retire and die.

I was working on a patient who had appendicitis when Dr Edams walked in, my friend who I was talking about. He signalled to me to come so I left the job to some others and came out.

"Patient's just been called in. It's a special case. He was shot in the chest whilst coming out of a bank. Shot by accident it seems, but Police are dealing with the little commotion. It's David Hullman."

I stopped taking off my medical gloves and looked at him.

"David?" He nodded slightly. I looked at my feet then

breathed in deeply. David was my cousin and a leading doctor in the surgery.

I ran to the theatre.

I was in there 8 hours fixing him up. It was a tough shot and he was lucky to be alive. His wife didn't visit. I didn't know why. Edams came up to me.

"How is he?"

"Oh fine, fine." He sat down, thinking.

It was a stuffy room, with two non-openable windows on either side of the roof. There was a door in front of me and kids' pictures on the wall. The fan on the ceiling had stopped working. Electricians had come to fix it, but all they had done was widen the crack on the ceiling. Whenever I went into the room, my eyes were hypnotised by the crack. I was always uneasy in that room whether the ceiling might fall on my head or not.

I looked at Edams. I had to break the silence.

"That shot must've been fired from quite close. Otherwise it would've been less huge." I stood up and switched off the blaring television in the corner. Edams still sat, staring at it in thought.

"I'll go and see if he's alright." I made to leave, his words stopped me.

"David's dead."

I felt that I had failed, in that one second of unbelieving, I felt I was wrong.

"The cops took out his life support system. They gave us eight thousand to compensate and told us to keep smiling."

I walked over to my chair and flopped down in it. The crack was the only presence in the thick, unseen silence, the two of us sitting like dead men.

"Why?" and the atmosphere went.

"I don't know," managed Edams.

"You let them get away with it," my voice was rising. "You let them quietly assassinate him like suffocating a baby."

"What were we meant to do? Yell 'No' and let them destroy the hospital. That's what they would've done."

We were both yelling now. I looked at him. He was shaking, not with rage, but with the tears that he was keeping in him. I left him crying and walked to my office.

I became a thinker that day.

I went to the bank where the shooting took place and looked around. It was my lunch break and I'd slipped out of the meeting that commenced. It would be about David, I guessed.

The bank was surrounded by police, their visors reflecting the sun. No press was there and I realised I was the only person looking at the steps. Others were just hurrying by without a backward glance. They weren't uninterested. They were scared.

"Please move away sir," an iron tight voice informed me.

I moved, still looking and then merged into the crowd, feeling the visors were watching me all the way.

I went to the library and there I looked at the files on everyone in the city. I had my ID and said I was researching all possible victims of a disease. I climbed on the little movable ladder and looked under Hullman.

There was nothing, just two files of John and Michelle Hullmen leaning together.

I then heard a buzz on the radiocom. It was especially loud as it was coming from a box just above my ear.

"Would ID number 48651 please report to the library desk as some gentlemen wish to speak with him."

I lay still for some time, cold with fear. Maybe these were the same people that David . . . Oh God.

I dismounted the ladder carefully, knowing that there was

no way I could get out of the warehouse-like building without being caught. There was only one way in and one way out. I walked to the library desk slowly, knowing millions of little eyes were watching me.

There were eyes in the hospital as well, eyes everywhere, covering walls where everyone usually walked. The worst part was that nobody saw them. They were hidden eyes.

I came to the desk and saw the two men. They both wore black raincoats and one was bald and had deep dark glasses. The other had a slight moustache and a beard. When they saw me, they walked towards me.

"Please don't be alarmed. I am Michael Puer and this is Elmer Windcoop. You seem to have presented us with a little problem. Please, remember that David Hullman died of his wounds and his wife fell down the stairs. Also, from now on, your ID card is banned from the library and if you use it again, you will be arrested."

The bearded Michael walked away and Elmer looked at me for a few minutes before walking away.

I was an outsider after that.

The people at the hospital congratulated me on my successful operations and then left me. The secretaries no longer hailed a "Good morning Doctor Kales". Edams started to talk to me less and less. I felt worthless and destroyed. My life's ambition had no point and I felt like a dog chasing his tail round and round again and again until the day he dies.

Hullman's funeral was scheduled for the 12 of October. He was to be buried along with his wife at the church at Littlestanton.

On the 9th, I saw a broadcast about the next election. It was two men, Hoffa Day-Lew and Forcart Arkle against each other and Superon. Hoffa looked good and I was planning to vote for him.

On the 10th Hoffa was found dead in his back garden, his wife dead in the bath.

I knocked on Edams' door and opened without reply. He was on the phone and immediately pardoned the caller and stopped as I came in.

"What do you want?" He was nervous, as if I was a wild beast.

"I want to borrow your ID card."

He looked at me sadly and I hated him for it.

"Give me the Goddam card!!!"

He shook his head.

"I could get killed if I give this to you." He was holding the card after fishing it out of his pocket. "You could get killed." He looked scared, very genuinely scared of me. He passed it over and I left. I heard him nervously typing at his desk as I put on my coat and walked out.

It was raining and I was soaked as I entered the Library. The area around the desk had lots of radiators and I warmed myself up on one of them as I watched the people on the left look at the books. On the right was the file room.

A young teenager went up to the secretary and asked her something. She left with him and immediately I was over to her little compartment and under the desk. I eventually found the camera switch and turned it off. I pulled out some of the plugs as well and then ran through the automatic steel doors into the file room.

The computer was on the right hand side and I ran to it.

Please enter pass code.

I squinted at Edams' card and read "63271".

Thank you.

Card accepted.

The list of files was endless, but I knew what I was looking for.

Hullman.

It clicked a bit and then read:

Sorry sir. No Data can be found on that name.

I then scanned through the files and saw my name.

It suddenly deleted.

I looked up. The eyes were on now, and all looking at me. I glanced through the doors and saw Michael and Elmer talking to the secretary and then coming into the files room.

"Sorry for the inconvenience, Ladies and Gentlemen, but due to a slight technical hitch, we must ask you to evacuate the building. Evacuate. Evacuate the building."

I hid round a corner as they came in. I then slipped round to one of the aisles between the rows of files, as they started at the top. I walked slowly so my tread wouldn't sound and then reached the ladder.

Michael appeared in front of me.

He was standing very still, the gun in his hand aimed very clearly at my head.

"Sorry Dr Kales, but we have found need to terminate your stay in the city." It sounded so robotic, so perfect as if it had been rehearsed and said many times. I was almost in a dream as I dropped down to the floor as the bullet whizzed over my head and into Elmer, who was standing behind me. He flew backwards for a short second and then landed on the floor with a sickening thud.

Michael fired again, but I flung myself upwards at the ladder and rolled it along, the bullet embedded in its iron steps. I knocked over Michael and then ran out of the file room, joining the trail of pedestrians leaving.

That night I became the most wanted fox in all of the hunt.

Articles were printed in every newspaper of how I shot Elmer Windcoop and wounded Mr Puer. I was sad as I read it on the underground to hear that the hospital had been severely disabled by my action. Now hardly anyone would use it.

I didn't hear anything, but I knew Edams was dead. It was a fact that added to my hatred of the society our city lived in. I wasn't really reading the paper, just sitting, thinking.

There was a war going on. The thinkers against the Law. I wondered if you could call it that, if you could call it a group of people who shoot anyone who comes near the truth or who gets in their way.

I didn't think you could. This city is Justiceless. I've never seen a moment of Justice since I was born here. I was trapped before this. As soon as you're born in this city, you're trapped. Trapped by the unambitious way of life. Trapped by the law. And you can never leave.

Once someone tried to drive out of here in a car.

It was blown up by the police.

The tube stopped and I got out, leaving my paper. I went straight to one of the underground pubs that avoids the law and I ordered a room. I went and sat at a table in the corner, away from all the hookers and drugs. I drank my drink slowly. I looked at the man on the table next to mine.

He was looking at me. Pondering me. I wondered who he was and then tucked my face deeper into my coat. When I looked out of my coat, he was sitting opposite me, drinking cheerfully.

"You the Kales man?" It was a hushed whisper.

"Yes," I said, figuring I had nothing to lose.

"I'm Barry Kembell. Leader of the SABOC."

"SABOC?"

"Society Against the Barons Of Change."

Then I understood. The Barons of Change is Superon's party. Was Superon's party. I finished my drink and then looked at him.

"So what do you do?"

"Try to find the truth. We've been watching Superon's house . . . fortress I should say, for 10 months now and we're planning a raid on the 12th."

David's funeral.

Tomorrow.

It was pitch black that night. The road was lit up by fluorescent lights which cast an eerie glow over all the road. There was no traffic as the normal people were at home, getting ready, as usual, for bed.

They had their smart timetables and schedules. We had a rough plan of how to invade a manor house smothered in Guards and Police from head to toe.

Kembell was not friendly. He was a genius at quick thinking and a good leader, but not what you'd call friendly. I had known him only a day however and was already holding an LB 10 machine gun after some vague training in how to use it.

It started at 11.

Kembell gave the signal and his troops swelled up the slight hill to Superon's house.

The lower half was bombarded by grenades and the guards had a fierce battle with his men. The distant sirens of Police were coming nearer as I gripped onto the side of the house and made my way up to the roof. A man called Leighton was already there and he'd set a bomb on the roof. We dropped into the hole and I was told to go left and him right.

The corridors were very narrow and high, and I was always looking around me, suspecting anything. I heard a yell and a scream behind me, and then nothing. At the end of the passage was a sound-proof door that led to the stairs.

I whirled round and saw Michael, Leighton's body at his feet. I shot him until I had no bullets left and then I dropped my gun and walked towards Michael. He was dying and I watching him roll over and then breathe no more.

126

There was a door to my left and I walked through it.

Inside was a bedroom. No one lay in the bed, but there were loads of photos pinned on the walls of the bedroom and they seemed to all show Superon.

Next to the bed was a filing cabinet. I opened it and found only one file.

That was Superon Dalgleish's.

I opened it out and read.

SUPERON DALGLEISH

SUPERON BECAME THE FOUNDER OF A GROUP CALLED THE BARONS OF CHANGE. HE FOUNDED THE POLICE FEDERATION WE HAVE TODAY AND HE AND THE BARONS OF CHANGE TOOK OVER THIS CITY.

UNFORTUNATELY, IN 2306, HE SUFFERED A HEART ATTACK AND WAS NEVER THE SAME AFTER THAT. HE BECAME OBSESSED WITH DEATH AND THE IDEA OF JUSTICE. HE MADE THE POLICE SWEAR A SHOOT TO KILL POLICY AND TIGHTENED JUSTICE RIGOROUSLY. HE WAS A COMMUNIST WHO WAS ON THE BRINK OF STARTING A WAR WHEN HE HAD TO BE PUT INTO A MENTAL HOSPITAL BY THE ORDERING OF DR PHILIP EDAMS. HE DIED IN A MENTAL HOSTAL AFTER A LOBOTOMY IN 2312.

CLASSIFIED CLASSIFIED CLASSIFIED CLASSIFIED CLASSIFIED

Kembell burst in then and took the document off me.

War followed, and eventually the people won and then left the city.

I am now one of the chief doctors at New Dover. My past and history, however, is classified.

It never ends, never will end. Society can have its gods. I just make sure I don't become one.

Saad Choudhary (14)

*Ephesus

It used to be boring.
It's not anymore.
It now gives a feeling that cannot be written.
It used to mean nothing.
It means a lot more now.

I used to think nothing of walking on a dirty cobbled road
And seeing huge boulders in a pattern that seemed more
    like memory than something practical or useful.
I thought it more useful to walk on a pavement as at least
    it was not broken and totally useless.
It meant nothing.
It definitely means more now.

When younger and enjoying myself on holiday in Turkey
I was told that instead of the beach
We would visit a lifeless land of equally lifeless rock
Called by the scholarly name of *Ephesus*.
It was met with a groan and a whole lot more.
When I got to Ephesus and went on a guided tour it still
    seemed unnecessary.
It does not feel unnecessary anymore.

When it was too late and I was leaving Turkey
I thought deeply about seeing one of the seven wonders of
  the world.
Then also seeing the temples, theatres, culture and religion
  of two thousand years ago
I wondered why I was deeply touched by this unnecessary
  feeling.

I was unlikely then to put my feelings on paper.
For it was an unknown feeling but a wondrous one
To walk where old civilisations had walked before,
To sit where old civilisations had sat before,
To dream of the past as they had dreamt of the future.
I dreamt of them as they had dreamt of me.

I don't know why it means something now but it does.
It is not unnecessary, boring or stupid anymore.
Yet I cannot say why.

What I can say is I will visit that place again and each time
  get a deeper feeling than the time before.
In the future I will again walk through those great blessed
  gates
And visit that wondrous, amazing and partly divine place
  again.

Richard Ray (11)

*Halstat

I remember Halstat. It clings
by its finger-tips
to the towering peaks of the Dachstein,
its feet lost in the black,

silent waters of the lake.
Stilted houses paddled
in the shallows, their legs
petrified and blackened with age.

A shaft of light falls
on the decorated homes
of the townspeople.

A fountain splashed
by the bone-house where
painted skulls and thigh-bones lay
in the gloom of the cave-like crypt.

Emily Fleuriot (16)

*Suspended Near My Ceiling – Thoughts In Symbols

Sometimes things get a bit strange. I am always afraid of the poltergeist, so when I am alone I try to close my mind to anything else. When I am doing this the ceiling is the back-drop for my thoughts. Covering every wall of my room are the usual things, the posters, the pictures, everything that is me. Sometimes I am not me and I am not sure who is me. I think this is why the ceiling is the most serene part of my rather hectic home. It is creamy in colour and dappled like a gently rippling pool. Only a tiny sea of tranquillity, but at least it is. Despite everything that I do my mind never becomes blank. There are always thoughts, sliding in, through the seams of my head. Little memories, ideas, ques-tions, worries. The worries are what I fear the most. How should I cope with a great problem? I should not be able to think any longer. Thinking about this nothing will ever become entirely clear, however much I cleanse the whirring of my head. Even if I could be rid of everything there is a trinity that never fails to arrive.

When I gaze at my ceiling these are the three things that I see all the time – a sword, a creature and a bottle endlessly filling a glass. They are all connected to one another in a perverted triangle. They all move in their own way, they cannot move away from this triangle, so spend most of the time that I see them in more or less the same spot. They are somewhere near the ceiling, and somewhere near to my body; suspended in mid-air by invisible thread. I lie in the middle of the triangle, scrutinising each corner in turn. The three corners of my mind. I say that they are my mind because I am sure that is what they are: my feelings, my needs, my wants. Even when I must not think, for fear of the poltergeist, I am made to. It is a cruel trick, a cruel game. But I am allowing it, going against all my own wishes.

One of the corners is the sword. It is sleek and luminous, of a luminosity that could glow truly, maybe one day it will shine. It is not a sharp sword, the tip does not glint, it has been blunted through years of betrayal, mishandled. The sword cannot cut, but it can glide through things, find holes and fill them. It is smooth and cool to caress, I would bite it if I could reach it. Could I even touch it if I reached high enough? I do not think so. It is something that can never be touched, never controlled. Any attempt to do so would turn it to molten gold and slip through my fingers, it could backfire dangerously. It is the only one of the three which rarely moves. It quivers sometimes, but only when I am happy, almost agitatedly so. I wonder if it should worry me that it does not move more, that it does not slice through the tri-angle. At the moment I am not, but maybe one day I will be.

The creature, in comparison to the sword, moves vigor-ously. It is not any kind of animal from the true world. It is like a dog, but it isn't, it has a longer body than a dog, and is also round. It looks as though it has skin like rubber, not fluffy, no fur. The dog was not created by me alone. There was an outsider who helped. Because of this there is another type of life, another attitude, from the creature. It is not my own in entirety. It is happy, jumpy, almost vivacious. Its feelings sometimes transfer to me, as if the dog were caressing my leg. From the dog exudes a desperate longing for escape. I can feel it wanting to leave its station, stretch the boundaries of the triangle. It gazes at my door, but attempting to leave causes the dog to rotate around and around on the axis of its line. It cannot leave though. None of the three may leave until I am ready for them to do so. When we first materialised the dog, it would roll over and over. I had to concentrate very hard, think very slowly, for it to stop this. Now the dog goes forward in movement only, there is no more entertainment in futile games. But it can never be totally controlled, it is still bright in colour, and it has a wicked kink in its tail.

The final corner is the strangest, the most puzzling. It is the corner that I am least sure of. It must be a strange message if I do not understand it myself. Both the bottle and the glass are clear, looking pure as crystal. Appearances can be deceptive, many things can be alike to that beauty. Sometimes they quiver together, as one, though one is the input and one the receiver. Other than the slight tremors which are carried to me over the air, the only movement is between the neck and the rim. The bottle continuously pouring something of a liquid state. The cup does not ever fill, yet I see the contents moving towards it. The bottle is empty yet it always strives to fill the endless chasm that is the cup. It seems to be a constant suspension, something inattentive. It is stuck in that movement; pouring has commenced, and can never cease. I watch from below, through the two objects, fickle in their appearance. There is a solidity that could stop this, but it is not allowed by either the cup or the bottle. They are curiously attached.

All three take over my body, preventing meditation. The sword is somewhere at the back of my mind, and until I allow the connections to take place, it is largely ignored. The creature sends my body into internal convulsions. I despair at my lack of control, yet delight in the ability to be unbridled. The glass and bottle are the most inexplicable, the most painful. They pound at my heart, blackening and bruising, though they do not touch my physical body.

What am I escaping from when I think this? Is it myself or the others that is more frightening? It is easier to remain sane by yourself. There is no one to contend with, no one to suffocate you, hold you back from your desires. There is reason to make thoughts against the backdrop of the ceiling, it is a purer colour than anything that has tried to live in this world.

> "The wasps cover my hands
> and my eyes.
> They enter my mouth
> and my lungs.
> They call it reality."

Sarah Tandy (13)

What is Normal?

Foreigners in cities,
Lost and alone,
People on the streets,
Who have no home,
What is normal?

The blind and the deaf,
The rich and the poor,
The families destroyed,
By bloodshed and war,
What is normal?

The man up the road,
Who just lost his wife,
The murderers in jail,
Locked up for life,
What is normal?

The clever, the stupid,
The large and the small,
The fat and the thin,
And the short and the tall,
What is normal?

Me and my friends,
My family my home,
I am not unhappy,
Afraid or alone,
Is that normal?

BLACK ARROW FENCERS

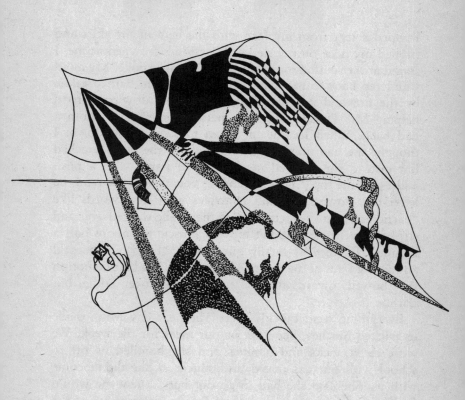

Joanna Falcon (16)

Rosemary Hall (12)

The Other Mother

I wiped a tear from my face with the hem of my skirt and rubbed my nose on my sleeve. Miss Jones frowned at me. I stared at the scuffed toe of my shoe. No one spoke. My mind wandered back to the night before. Mum had bathed Eddie by the fire and put him to bed. I'd been down the road helping Mrs Davids with her shelves – she suffers from a bad back. When I came in, Mum told me to sit down. I thought she had maybe found out about the cup I cracked but instead she showed me a piece of paper with a posh address at the top. "They're sending you away." She read the letter out slowly, the long sentences with long words like "participate" and "evacuation" in them. She walked over and stroked my fringe. I didn't move a muscle for about half a minute. "Ed too?" I finally questioned. "Ed too," she said and walked out of the room. That was the last bit of emotion she showed towards me really. She fussed over Eddie, but not me.

Everything went quickly then. The next day Mum made us packed lunches. She gave us our meat for the week. We wore clean socks and hankies and she bundled us off to school with our gas masks and suitcases. She didn't come with us. She said she had to go out but I knew she would find it too hard to say goodbye to Ed. As we went out of the door she kissed him. "Look after him, Janet," she said sternly. I felt a flash of jealousy before putting my hands on his shoulders and marching him down the road.

Now we were on the train. The steady motion comforted me as I thought of all the things I would miss. I felt a few more tears trickle past my nose as I thought of Mrs Davids. I hadn't even said goodbye.

When the train jolted to a stop, we were at a deserted station. It wasn't much more than a platform really. We walked down a dusty road. Ed took hold of my hand and whispered, "It's so clean." I smiled for he was right. When I breathed in there was a lovely fresh smell. Ed tired soon so I told him to spot colours. It was amazing. We saw the lush greens, the oranges and the yellows of the leaves and the splashes of pink and blue flowers in the verge.

Eventually, we arrived at a big hall. Inside we were lined up. For about an hour we were washed and checked and spooned medicine.

Then some people came in. After about twenty minutes, a sturdy man entered. He pulled me out of the line. Miss Jones said, "She has a little brother." So the sturdy man rather reluctantly pulled Eddie towards us and shoved us both into a cart. It was dark by now and very cool and still outside. We were taken to a cottage about a mile away. The man didn't ask our names. He didn't introduce himself. He led us into a little room at the back of the cottage. It had two beds, a cupboard and a rug in it. He said gruffly, "Be quiet", and left the room.

Ed began to cry. I helped him get into his pyjamas and got into bed myself. "It'll be all right, Eddie," I whispered over and over again into the darkness.

In the morning, I woke to see the most beautiful face looking at me. She smiled at me. I sat up and glanced around. Ed was asleep, the corner of the sheet in his mouth. "I'm Mrs Ash, but you can call me Aggie," she said. Her voice was sweet and clear. "I'm Janet." I couldn't help but look at her. Her blonde hair was tied back behind her neck but little wisps fluttered out. Her eyes were deep blue, her cheeks were pink and her skin was creamy and smooth. "Get dressed, Janet, and come and have some breakfast." I did, and breakfast was a delicious luxury. I had a fresh egg and bread and fresh milk. As the day wore on, Aggie was so kind to Eddie and me. She asked us about ourselves and told us a little about herself. I realised that she spoke almost nothing of her husband. She told us that his name was John and that was all. That evening she showed us a book with flowers in it. She was just saying that by the stream you could get the pretty pink ones when the door opened and John strode in. I saw the cheerful prettiness vanish from her face. "Janet." Her voice was small. "Take Edward to your room."

I was scared. I knew John had been drinking. We smelt it on his breath. I closed the door behind us and rushed into our room. Ed cried again that night. We didn't see Aggie or John, but we heard John. He was shouting. I couldn't make out what he was saying – his speech was slurred, but he was very angry. He threw chairs around and I could hear crockery smashing. I pictured Aggie crouched in the corner, speechless and defenceless, maybe crying.

I woke again to see her lovely face. She didn't mention the night before. If he had broken things, you couldn't see. All looked peaceful in the house.

That day we had to go to school. Aggie walked us down the road to it. At the gate, she touched my shoulder. "Good luck, Janet," she said. Something glowed inside me. I had received individual attention over my younger brother. I smiled at her and she smiled back – an encouraging, loving smile.

School was far too crowded. The one classroom had four classes in it. Obviously Ed and I were split up. I was quite clever. I could read and write well. I paid attention and worked hard. School had always been an escape route from my problems, Mum favouring Eddie usually. Now though, I was escaping from the thought of John hurting Aggie. For the way that she changed when he walked in was enough to tell me that it had happened many times before.

There were a few fights at break. I kept Eddie well clear. He would be slaughtered in a fight. He's small and skinny.

Aggie was at the gate when the last bell went. "You didn't have to come, Aggie," I protested. "I know the way." She smiled at me, the same loving smile. "I wanted to."

Quite quickly, we fell into a routine. Breakfast was always tasty. School was bearable. Aggie picked us up and we would go back to the cottage. I would help her with the tea and Eddie would play outside. At about six o'clock each evening, John would return. We didn't know what he did all day and we couldn't ask but when we heard the door, we learnt to go straight to our room where we tried to sleep through the abuse.

We had been there about a month when, one day after school, Aggie wasn't at the gate. We waited for her but after ten minutes we went back to the cottage.

The door was open. I pushed it, cautiously, and went in. The room was a shambles. Plates, chairs and ornaments were broken on the floor. "Go out and play, Edward." I used his full name so he would know I was serious. He dropped his satchel and disappeared out of the door. I had to find Aggie. She was in the kitchen, repeating hysterically, "He doesn't normally come in the day", over and over again. I calmed her down. As we began to clear up the mess, she told me how he had been such a gentleman when they had married six years ago. The drink and the talk of war with his rowdy mates had roughened him. "Will we have to go?" I asked tentatively. She nodded. "There's no war anyway." Suddenly, I began to cry. She put her arms around me and

John found us there an hour later – two sobbing bodies clinging to each other. He hit me as well that night. I wouldn't leave her side. I tried to protect her but he was too strong.

Several evacuees from the village went back on the same train as us. They all laughed and joked, telling stories of those "stupid country people". I sat in the corner, with a heavy heart, already missing the golden wisps of my other mother.

Heather Macnaught (16)

**Son Like a Boy

Her son like a boy
was a lesser son
than her first
His skin was like praline
He had grimy hair
which lashed his cheek
She loved her boy
because he was hers
unlike her first
Her first son kissed concrete butt
and dialled a phone
He had a smart costume
But her son like a boy
wore bare flanks
and his hair grew more
The first son never called
her on his handy phone
Her lesser son
called her by shouting
across the water from his den
Her fond looks on him
Her proud hand upon him
The first son gained no mother
but a clenched deal, a clenched fist
and a passed business incentive
He passed over his roots
while his brother ate them

That serious son clapped ironheels
on the street where he cruised
Her son like a boy
clapped his hands and heels
as he heard music on those same streets.
He juggled fire and consumed flames
His dreaded hair snake-danced to beats and flutes
The elder son juggled shares
and consumed convenience food
His face was a snake that beat
the flute out of everyone
His exterior was his interior
He had no face
Through the lesser's dirty exterior
Shone a sun, like her boy
Her lesser but real child
With all his naked grace.

Sarah Morning (15)

*Scottish Widow

I am forty-four and unaccustomed to love. I dream about the nature of death. I dream about my husband. Not like a normal wife. Normal wives imagine the sanctity of lying in bed after nights of passion. I dream about lying in our bed after his funeral. I dream of his death – in a freak storm on a mountain, strangled by one of his dirty socks or poisoned by his home-made beer.

It beats me how monks keep their vows of silence. In my experience of men, God has in-bred this species with universal bodily sounds. Alastair's at this moment is the gentle, dull scrape as he picks ear wax out with the leg of his specs. To his right sits our first son, Alex, who is noticeably snorting mucus through his sinuses. However I try to ignore the sounds and look to the positive side – at the rate he's going there will be one less mouth to feed tonight. Our second and third sons, Graham and Michael, are following suit, eating apples by drowning them with saliva. My family. I love to hate them or I hate to love them. Either way they don't care. As long as I feed them.

Whilst my father sits in the kitchen alone, my husband and sons sit in the lounge "bonding" in front of Match of the Day. Thus it is left to me to clean up the pools of sick coagulating in Michael's room, hide convincingly the cigarette ash and porn magazines in Alex's room and dispose of Graham's needles – my kids aren't all they're cracked up to be. It has become a routine ritual of protecting my father from knowing that Graham's chances of getting his highers are diminishing fast, so too is any hope of Michael getting past the end of this year without expulsion and the only computer degree Alex is likely to get is one in hacking.

"Tea alright Dad?" I asked him. "Ay Myra tea's fine," he replied in his usual compromising manner. I've always struggled to communicate with my father, I'm the first to admit it. But now, now it's even harder. For he has it known that any mention of sex, women, politics or the fortunes of Glasgow Rangers brings on his ulcers. So I am left every week with only two scintillating topics with which to construct an adequate conversation – cooking or television. And since he disapproves of televisions we only ever broach topics together such as why pizzas and spicy foods bring on ulcers. However as usual to my relief he tends to doze off at this point.

"Dad, Dad, milk in your tea?" He awoke with a grunt and the eloquence of a tractor in reverse. "No, no Myra you know I have my coffee black," he said. I insisted it was tea that he wanted. "No . . . Myra . . . not tea I know I asked for coffee." Stubborn silence. "But if you've made your tea now . . . I suppose I'll have to have it . . . sweet tea mind, has to be sweet." And so I gave him his *sweet* tea. And in return he said, "Oh Myra! You've put sugar in my tea! You know how it affects my ulcers."

Alastair is an "executive computer programmer". It was midnight before he arrived home every night this week. I asked him why – as a caring wife concerned for his well-being. Said he'd had to do some important hole-punching with the secretary before it got on top of him.

It was me that had to drive the family to the mountain. Alastair had lost his licence for drunk driving a week ago on his way home. I told him I fully understood and how I thought the judge would be lenient when he had explained his predicament. After all hole-punching affects people in different ways. It was Alastair that had suggested this

146

"family" outing. Alastair the shepherd had soon disappeared over the hill with his faithful flock admiring and following him. Literally following in his every footstep by standing in no doubt everything that he had. Meanwhile Miss Bo Beep was slumped at the bottom of the mountain indulging in a quick cigarette, contemplating the extra washing Alastair's ego trip had cost her.

I waited for an hour for the four wise men to return. But they didn't.

They had left me with the dog. They didn't want her. Alex had said to his father, "She's too old, she'll cramp our style, anyway she's had enough exercise for today, poor bitch." Sitting at the bottom of the "mountain" out of breath, cigarette in one hand, I wasn't sure whether he was referring to me or the dog. Probably both of us. And when Columbus and his crew didn't return, I didn't really care.

I was down to my last four cigarettes when I registered that they had been gone for over two hours. So it must have been on my seventh when I began to wonder. Perhaps they had gone. Lost in the mist.

Two left and I really did begin to believe they had gone. Lost in the Scottish mountains or attacked by a Scottish maniac living in the highlands. After that point I did panic – I was on my last cigarette and only one pound to buy another pack. Then either my conscience or my habit took over. I descended the mountain. It must have been the need for Nicotine that drew me down. It couldn't have been the love for my family.

Nor was it the love for my family that took me to the telephone for help. I suppose it was the realisation that it would be blatantly obvious to the police when they enquired, why I hadn't contacted the emergency services. I mean I could hardly reply, "Yes officer was it really five hours? Well I actually spent my remaining one pound on a packet of cigarettes, rather than rescue my family." Even though I wanted to.

It was a local Scottish "tavern" that I wandered into on my errand of mercy. A lonesome Scottish Widow. "My whole family Vicar I know. Terrible news, but I intend to be strong – for their sakes." Yes, a Scottish Widow, the freedom suits me fine. Or would have. The figure had already appeared. The leg of his glasses sticking out of his ear. Alastair. He and the boys slumped in the corner behind a table contemplating another round. "Myra . . . what kept you so long. It got a bit cold, so me and the boys thought we'd shelter."

So it's back to my cell. I am forty-four and unaccustomed to love. I dream about the nature of death. I dream about my husband. Not like a normal wife. Normal wives imagine the sanctity of lying in bed after nights of passion. I dream about lying in our bed after his funeral. I dream of his death – in a freak storm on a mountain, strangled by one of his dirty socks or poisoned by his home-made beer.

Esther Ingham (16)

The Aftermath

I sat in the corner
listening carefully to their silence,
hearing the multitude of accusations
and threats pass between them.
I heard my mother inwardly howl
and my father's sarcastic laugh.
Neither of them heard me.

She busied herself around the room,
every now and then looking at him
like a puppy that doesn't understand why
it's being punished.
He scornfully watched her,
contemptuous of her love and loyalty.

Emily Fleuriot (16)

*Unwanted Intimacy
A Short Story In Two Parts

PART I: HISTORY

I've been watching this woman for a while, from the hill at
the back of her house. She hasn't noticed though – I'm too
far away – she just sits there. Sits there drinking her coffee,
eating her breakfast. Usually it's toast, today she's eating an
egg. A smooth brown egg. She cracks it, slipping her knife
around it, the yolk oozes down its side, thick and glutinous
like lava. She still looks bored – a little dreamy – she doesn't
need her life. She's mine, I know how she moves. I watch her
dress; watch her come and go; I know her children. Her
nightdress is shiny like her glimmering eyes. I've seen her
eyes close once – they were beautiful, like my mother's only
more . . . I saw her in a shop – stood opposite her. If I stand
opposite her again she can recognise me, acknowledge me.

I'll go and visit her in her house, surprise her. I know how
to get in there, planned a secret route. I won't go through
her front door, I'd be like everyone else. She'll laugh, a
twinkly laugh, she'll remember.

I'm in her house but she can't see me yet. I've the courage
to speak to her now. I'm sure that she can feel me, so I'll
meet her in the hall. It's red and white how I imagined it to
be. She's walking to me, and I'm above her. I'll make her
jump, whisper in her ear.

She has switched on the light, but she's trembling, she's
afraid of something, what of I'm not sure. She doesn't realise
that it's me – I have to reassure her. She wants to leave the
house, I can see her looking at the door. She shouldn't leave.

150

We want to create our own world. I'm embracing her, she's stiff, not relaxed. She's afraid someone will see, find out. Not because it is wrong or ugly, but others could think so with their polluted minds. We should go upstairs, no one could see us there. We're upstairs.

She wants to scream, she's not comfortable here either. Her eyes dart around looking everywhere, except at me, her brow sweats. She's afraid of . . . she wants to stay with me, she must. She's not strong enough, not yet, she wants me but has to stay where she is. Why I don't understand. I shall let her go, forever, forget . . . . . .

Her rich thick blood is dispersing across the carpet. You can't see the red but you can see the wet. It could be water or tea but I know it's blood. Her body shook and she now lies still. She wants to be alone, I'll leave her lying here, she's at peace with herself now. Maybe I'll come back when she's ready.

PART II: HERSTORY

I'm in the kitchen. The melancholy clouds drift past my view through my window. They're aimless, go where told. I feel like that sometimes. I can feel the rain swelling within them, cracking thunder, shots of lightning. I can hear bangs. But they aren't outside, it's not the weather, no not . . . it's inside my house. Upstairs. Can't be the kids, they've only just left, and anyway I'd've heard them . . . Definitely, something is upstairs in the bathroom, or the bedroom. I must be wrong, I'm being silly . . . no, I'm not. There's a step on the stairs, another. I can hear them squeaking. They've stopped, I must be going mad. Just drink your cup of tea. I'll go next door and get Sam. Out the back door. The front's past the stairs. The key's not in the lock. I can't get out of the back. I'll just stay or . . . I'll go out of the front. I'm being stupid now, the footsteps stopped, but I'll unlock the back door anyway. Where are the keys? In the living room. Hunt the keys again. I can feel someone behind me in the hall, don't move. It's behind me, above my head. Don't turn around . . . front door . . . just to be on the safe side? Switch on the light, yes that's better . . . relax, calm down . . .

There's something on my shoulder, slipping around my throat, smooth leather, the smell fills my nostrils, my head. Don't hurt me. Please don't hurt me. Another hand around my head, covers my mouth. I feel a knife somewhere. He hushes me, like a baby. The baby that I am, I am helpless. What does he want from me? He's taking me up the stairs, dragging, cradling. Into the dark. The colour of blood, confusion, my head drags away from my hands, the body. Everything is whirling. I can't move any more. Paralysed. My body knocked with every move. Rest.

He wants to talk to me. His eyes imploring, but not speaking. He's shaking his head. Maybe he wants to cry. I'm still afraid. Who is this person? Still I cannot speak.

There's a knife in front of my eyes. It's all that I can see. It glints, as hard and sharp as I am soft. Stop. "Stop!"

The rags in my mouth. I can't scream. Can't swallow. No escape. The rags choke me, make me gag. My eyes see nothing. I hear though. Sounds muffled. They threaten me, because they are there. Caring maybe, but blinded. All around me. Shadows turn the reds of my eyelids dark, to black. Black like dried blood. There's no grip around me any more, no grip at all.

Sarah Stringer (16)

**Coal Dust

We fight, you and I, like
scorpions over shade; the black arrow
fencers of the soul.

You lunge; fancy footwork on my part
before I can be parted, and both
are stung by the sun.

Striped by sun and shade, we pause
and realise reconciliation
ran away to an old oasis.

But we break the break and
scuttle back and forth to
the music of the crack of

our unwanted twin-ness.
Both live this callous romance,
looking for the true double.

You: black as salt;
I: white as this damp, dank
dribbling dusk of an evening.

We both wear the wasteful whipping.
You can't abide this shade unless
my flesh provides a

shadow; I can't live without
the reedy swish of
your salt black tail.

Alexandra Bennett (14)

Fairy-Tale

In the fairy-tale
You told me,
The heroine came out of a
Syringe
And sold herself to the
Hero.
You have no faith
In the happy ending;
The story has become a
Nightmare,
And in your eyes
The wicked witch is victorious.

Rebecca Yearling (15)

*The Scholars

Old men bend over older books,
And put old eyes to further strain.
Old hands examine fevered looks,
Producing notes from lovers' pain.
The scholars grope where poets ran,
Translating love with pedants' care.
The lines no longer rhyme or scan,
The ardour faded into air.

All serious, correct and staid;
All dressed in grey; all faces lined;
All stained with ink; all cuffs are frayed;
All youthful life left far behind.

The lines imprison dream and thought,
Love's passions turned to dusty grey.
Unwilling pupils stay untaught.
The words have nothing more to say.

Daniel Murray (10)

*Deadly Fans

I once saw a man
building a trench
with sandbags
and barbed wire.
He had a rifle
in his hand

"Why are you building
a trench?" I asked.
"Is it because:
Aliens are coming
to strangle you?

The Zulus want to
study your death?

Cannibals have invited
you to lunch?

Wild animals are coming
for dinner?

The dreaded head-shrinkers
are coming to shrink
your head?

You have fallen out
with the chief of
the killer tribe?"

156

"No," he said, "I'm a footballer
and I'm preparing for the
fans."

Then came a rumble of
feet, a howl of glee, and
a whole swarm of
autograph hunters, fans and
fan club members began
swarming over the trench
and at the footballer,
despite the defences.

When they left, the man
was left with kisses
on him.

"See," he said, "that's
why I built the
trench."

Hudheifa Akber Moawalla (13)

*Country Confusion

An Injured – only companion,
Keeping still and listening to its advantages and how it
    should
Be proud of being able to fly unlike other animals,
I myself pretending strongly to listen to its speech which
    is stalled
On and off by its injury,
The now wiry-looking creature makes me speechless as
    I stroked
Its uninjured head pitifully,
Why was I doing this?
I am a cruel farmer whom the children hate,
And here I am in the barn caring for the flying animal!

I suppose I should really change my ways,
For it is New Year!
Maybe I should shoot again like a sprouting tulip or
    broad bean.

Cathy Baker (12)

A Mirror of the Man

Benedict Barton was: not old, not young, around forty; a Social Security clerk, and typically overworked, as many of the breed are; one of the most traceable families in his village (although the impact of this was considerably lessened by the fact that he came into Canterbury to work), and a man who would never let people forget that.

But this was not all; for he was also a bigot, one of the most bigoted bigots that ever walked in Kent.

He was nasty: to everyone generally, but in particular to anyone not like him. Women, the black, Asian or poor: anyone who differed from him in any way bore the full brunt of his abuse.

And today was not a good day for Barton. His two underlings whom he despised (Miss Lake and Mr Patel) having both called in "sick", Barton himself was left having to take a post in the office, dealing with people and their worldly troubles as they came in. And so he had been inventing imaginary paperwork, cheques to sign, letters to write, envelopes to open.

He had found everything happening against him: his journey had been a walking hell, during which he had sneered at the Indian man trying to sell him a ticket, and sworn conspicuously at this man's voice when it crackled over the Tannoy. And then there had been the feeling of someone dogging his footsteps; in fury he had turned behind himself several times on being sure of having heard a breath or a footstep out of place: but it seemed as if the unseen offender had simply melted away into the crowd, because no likely suspect came to Barton's eyes.

And the escalator had been broken down at Canterbury station: he had been shepherded into a lift (he hated the infernal machines) and pressed up against two silly young Continental *au pairs* giggling and giggling. But at last he had been released, and in anger he jumped into his customary taxi. But once in there he could still feel the eyes on him: the driver could not be the culprit, for in strict accordance with the rules of the road he had eyes only for his journey. And Barton and he were alone in the car.

But at least now Barton was seated safely at his desk, that inviolable ship where he could not be disturbed. A quick riffle through the post would begin his day anew: bills, the electricity, a mis-addressed notice for Invoices across the hall, and an importunate leaflet seeming to lie alone, displaced from the others, as if it was a magnet repelling its like pole.

Something brought his hand to the leaflet first: he reached for it, but then drew his hand back as if he had been burnt.

"Don't pick it up!" he heard himself whisper, but he resisted himself and did so. He turned it over and over in his hands, and he felt it to be cold, colder than the chilling wind blowing outside.

And it was only now that he looked at the message on the leaflet: "Equality for All!" it enthused, the type of thing he put straight in the wastebasket. But some unknown force had impelled him to grasp the paper: and now against Barton's will the force slowly brought his fingers to the leaflet's middle, and made them throw it open to reveal its message.

"This Christmas Let Us Make The World Equal!" its big type proclaimed ecstatically. Barton had been right the first time: without leaving his chair he threw the seasonal missive into his wastebasket, smiling as it soared in without even clipping the municipal-green metal rim. Then, pleased, he left to make his regular trip to the office tea-machine.

Later, holding his steaming polystyrene cup, he sat back

down at his desk, and was surprised to see the equality leaflet in front of him. Surely he had consigned it to the bin?

He moved to pick it up, but threw himself back against his chair. There was something strange, unearthly, about his desk, his chair, his entire room.

"Goldberg!" he called suddenly, wishing that any kind of company would come to relieve him from this alien solitude. But no one came.

And then he looked down to see the leaflet lying in his lap, and realised in horror that when throwing himself away from it he had caught it with his fingers; instead of distancing himself from it he had brought it even nearer. He tried to throw it across the room, but his hand would not grip around it. Instead, he stood up to let the thing drop.

And as he saw it on the floor he also saw the figure on the front of the leaflet, saw it for the first time: it was to him a grotesque figure, half black and half white and blurring into grey in the middle, and in its shape the perfect image of . . . But Barton did not want to look any further, for in it he saw the slump of his own shoulder, the stoop of his own leg, the bend of his own arm: from the top of his head to the smallest toe, even to the cut of the shirt and the hook of the nose, it was himself.

"No!" Barton shouted in horror, and he brought his thick-soled brogue down on the offending picture as if it were a trespassing ant daring to cross his deep-pile floor.

But this, as it turned out, solved nothing, for at that moment, the door creaked open to reveal a shaft of light, and casting a shadow in the brilliant beam stood the exact figure from the leaflet.

"I welcome you, Benedict Barton," it said.

"Go away!" commanded its image. "You're not here. I can't see you."

"You know I'm here," said the figure. "You've known I

161

was here all day. I know all about you, Benedict Barton."

"About what?"

"You know about me. You knew I was here, you felt I was here. And you know why I have come."

"I don't. Why? What do you want with me?"

"Think of all those you have oppressed, Barton, think of all those you turn away each day. The young mother with three children. Just because she happens to be a different colour from you, you deny her what is her due."

There was no answer.

"The man, the old man who lost his leg in a factory accident many years ago. You neglect him. You don't see him. You don't help him up the stairs. Just because he has only one leg: just because the skin on that leg is a different colour."

"Enough!" Barton could stand it no longer. He threw himself at the figure: but although he saw his clenched fist connect with its target of the thing's jaw, he felt no impact, only the rush of empty air.

"What kind of beast are you?" he asked it.

"I am the essence of all those you have oppressed: I grow every day."

"Go away!" Barton ordered. "I'll change, I will! I'll do anything you say!"

"It is too late for resolutions. Watch me, Barton. Your time is past: you can do nothing about yourself."

And before Barton's very eyes the thing shimmered, until it was as if it were a mirror of the man. Not only their shape and clothes, but now their complexion and expression were the same: and as the new Barton took a seat at the first Barton's desk, it was as if all motion had been reversed. The first Barton (but now who could tell, and how? He might as well be the former Barton, the once-Barton: the two were identical in every shape and form) turned to run away, to break out into reality, but the new Barton held him back.

"I have not yet finished with you," he was saying, and then he seemed to point: and then the once-Barton knew no more.

Benedict Barton bent down from his chair to pick up a leaflet from the floor. The hint of a smile could be seen on his face as he looked at the slogan and the picture accompanying it.

"Let Us Stamp Out Men Like This!" it exhorted him: and there beneath it were a few insignificant words, and the picture of a man pointing to other pictures, the black and the old and the sick. But the expression on its face was something in itself: was it rage or fear, or something else entirely, which could not be explained?

It wore a suit and tie, and was neither old nor young: a clerk of some kind, and typically overworked, as the breed typically are. But that was not all, for the man depicted, in all but his beliefs, was the man reading the leaflet: the man was himself.

FOUR SHADOWS WALKED . . .

"Four
Shadows
Walked"

Jo Cannon (14)

Sarah Monroe (12)

*Someone Trod on my Grave Today

I was sitting at the supper table when death stole in,
Silently, stealthily, unnoticed, unassuming – no drama.
We were eating our salad – a family at argument.
Rivalry, discussion, comment on the papers,
(Which should not be read at mealtimes).
Laughter.
Together.
Someone trod on my grave today.

Headlines to debate; bodies in the river, thousands dead,
A plane in Pittsburg, hundreds killed,
Snipers fire, a nation slaughtered.
Death at one remove.
Dramatic, explosive, fragments and noise.
"Read all about it."

Then my mother's voice, "She wore lipstick today.
She never does. It was crooked.
There to defy death I think."
A casual comment across the table,
But I listen, attention caught.
A bubble of time, a shroud of silence.
A young mother dying, just streets away.

166

No drama, no headlines, no debate.
Death is months not minutes.
They look the same from the outside, just thinner.
The juice squeezed out of the family, no spurting laughter.
"Will there be dressing on the salad?"
Someone trod on my grave today.

Death sits at our table
He comes quietly in corners, finding cracks.

The rattles resumes.
"The last square of chocolate is mine."
My mother does an odd job.
She catches my eye and smiles.
Warmth, reassurance – but,
Someone trod on my grave today.

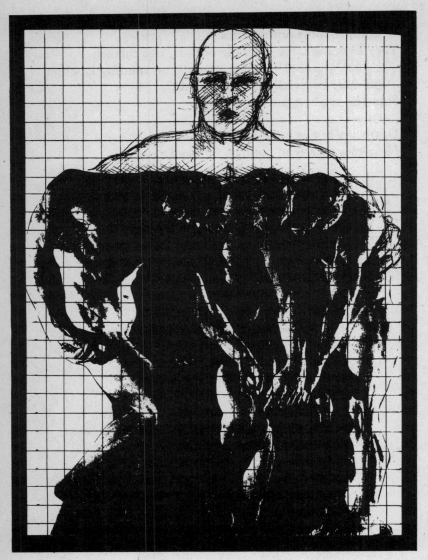

M. C. Anderson (16)

168

James Cowan (14)

Geriatric Ward

"My Darling Wife,
Another night has passed and another morning come and I
am still in the trenches and good health. What's that? Oh
Christ!"

"Don't shout now Mr Robbins, drink your tea!"

<u>The Battle of Loos</u>
<u>Casualties 25th Sept – 16th October 1915.</u>
<u>Killed and missing 15,800.</u>

One shadow stood and walked along the road from Rue
Bacquerat to Loos.

"Bloody mud, Bloody Wipers! For God's sake Bob – keep
your head down!"

"Mr Robbins! Don't tell me you've made a mess of yourself
again! Please!"

<u>Of a million men killed in the Great War,</u>
<u>250,000 fell in the few square miles around Ypres.</u>

Two shadows walked together along the road from St. Eloi
to Ypres.

"Blimey Charlie you've copped a Blighty one there! You'll be all right, just keep talking, keep awake! – Charlie?

"Is he still talking, keeping them all awake? Damned nuisance that Robbins is, Staff."

<u>Advance of Allied in the West Still Continues</u>
<u>Germans Driven Back in Disorder</u>
<u>A very satisfactory 1st Day – The Times 3rd July 1916</u>

Three shadows walked from Ploegsteert to Poperinghe.

"Why's it so dark, what's this mud on my face? I can't see, I can't see!!"

"For heaven's sake keep him quiet – he'll be on like this all night, you know him – blasted old fool!"

<u>Great Allied Attack – Ypres Salient Widened</u>
<u>Everywhere our objectives were attained – The Times</u>
<u>1st August 1917</u>

Four shadows walked on to Calais.

"Why was I left, why me? Boys? Hello Boys!"

"Trust him! When it's time for medicine he's asleep. Come on Mr Robbins! Mr Robbins?"

"It took us years to get over it. Years! Couldn't sleep,
couldn't lie still – tramped the streets till daylight.
That went on for years that did."
Rifleman F. White 10th Batt. KRRC.

Five shadows joined together – somewhere in France.

Luke Firmansjah (14)

December 31st, 1999

"Good evening. The outlook for tomorrow is
More Armageddon, I'm afraid,
And you can see this big band of
Mushroom cloud here, pushing its way in from
The East. Heavy firestorms will follow,
Sweeping across the mainland
With temperatures reaching
Ten million degrees Celsius in places
(That's fifty million degrees Fahrenheit) –
So get that six-hundred-thousand-factor sunblock
At the ready.

By the afternoon the situation will be like
This, with the possibility of radioactive
Showers in the North, and mutations
Occurring further south (outbreaks of
Leukaemia may follow in central areas).
Drivers are advised not to approach major cities,
And ships around the coast
Should be warned of the severe
Gale-force winds, exceeding
Six hundred miles-an-hour.

By Wednesday it would be a good idea to start
Wrapping up for the upcoming Nuclear Winter,
And these freezing conditions may continue
For the duration of the next millennium.
Chance of Fall-out is
One hundred per cent.
Good-night."

**Salvage in Boxes

It was a pile as big as a house; the wavering steps protruded
from the bulky accumulation like sticklebricks and I had to
climb quickly before the sinking was given too much of a
chance. Where it was I fell, I won't bother remembering, but
when I turned my head round I saw a human hand under an
old toilet. The skin was pale and rigid to touch. Repelled, I
had to pull it out from under the mound, it was a curiosity.
Then, the arm yanked right out, but it was plastic. I thrust
my own hand into the space and grabbed for the empty
socket. I hauled the thing out and it was whole; the face
winked its feathery eyelids; it had a puckered expression.

Silly Dolly, I called it – imagine getting stuck under a pile
of salvage. Then I wondered how Silly Dolly had crawled
under there in the first place. I decided she must have been
looking for shoes and somebody had tipped rubbish on her.
I put her in a pram and wheeled her to the other mounds for
her to pick good shoes and an umbrella too as it looked like
rain in the sky. I scrambled through some scrap until I found
a white T-bar shoe with little holes on the top in the shape
of butterflies. There was only one and it was missing a buckle.
Silly Dolly would have to find her own shoes. I kept the one
shoe and slung Silly Dolly into the air. She landed with a
crunch and I galloped off to find her.

"Silly Dolly!" I bellowed, but she didn't answer.

I found her soon enough among the *canaille* of the yard. I
hated her little face full of its scurvy and her clothes were
mangier than most would want. I already had loads of dollies
from this yard and they were better and had shoes too. Silly
Dolly had neither shoes nor much hair to brush. So, I left

174

her in a spin-dryer with her left eye dourly hanging out by a piece of black cotton. She only had one arm; she couldn't suck her thumb and hold her bottle at the same time and that was no good.

The fading of the eventide cautioned me and I gazed for a brief while at the musing glow seeping beyond the yard. I crouched down and fell tired. My knees were gouged and my dress was unravelling on one side. My welly boots had pulled my long woollen socks into short, wrinkled bundles around my ankles. It was past time to leave and return home empty-handed. My sullen walk took me towards the gate where, on my way, I saw an awkward bird lying spreadeagled on a forlorn range – its head was held down by a nappy pin. It was black like the top of the stove and I was thinking that someone must have wanted it for their supper, so I left it alone. As day permeated into night, the dead bird had made me peckish and my belly was smarting in its hollow pangs.

It was a sorry thing to leave the scrapyard with nothing to show; I watched feebly as the ground evaporated into a miasma of smudged mist. I couldn't leave unburdened, so I claimed the nearest piece of remnant from the slur. I hobbled to collect my bike with my right welly mangled from a fall and pedalled precariously up the road with a soggy cardboard box balanced on my hip.

Sarah Morning (15)

*Tin Soldiers

There is no ark to save the children ,
Buried alongside their innocence,
As the marching realm of the tin soldiers
Tramples on through democracy.

But the tin soldier himself,
He cannot weep for his actions,
He is too fearful of his tears,
The risk of corrosion
A rust that would conspire to his own destruction.

Where is the knowledge now?
Who has forgotten to tell
Those future bronze statues of victorious Generals,
That patriotic paper children,
Are of no threat to their trained tin soldiers?

But still the paper is torn,
And the tin scissors continue to cut,
Whilst the war-torn cries of the paper children,
Are lost, forgotten far below,
Beneath the next slice of metal artillery.

Ciara McKeown (15)

*My Brother Calman

"Don't talk to me about scruples, the thing's superb physics."
(Comment made after Hiroshima by Enrico Fermi, one of the nuclear physicists in America who produced the plutonium for the world's first atomic bomb.)

Lifting the basket, I made my way through to the back porch and began filling it with peat. Through the glass doorway, I caught the faint, but unmistakable glimmer of a mast light out on the Pentland Firth. Once the basket was full, I carried it back through to the kitchen, stacked some peat on to the fire, and went across to the window.

Around the bay, twilight was touching the hills and with the light beginning to fail, I could now distinguish three mast lights. From the swinging motion, it looked as if the boats were pitching heavily. They continued on a steady course towards Strath Point lighthouse, then as they reached the Point, the vessels altered course. Veering several degrees towards Port they swung round and as they did so, I saw the *Norseman* was slightly ahead. Her distinctive high bow and small square sail, a standing joke amongst the other fishermen, made my father's boat easy to identify.

Lachlan and Donald MacLeod's *Freedom* was directly astern and although I could not make out the third boat, I took it to be Angus MacLean's. They always fished together. Further out, other lights lay dotted along the horizon; it looked as if the whole fishing fleet was heading back.

Normally, when the catch was good, the boats stayed out all night and my father would be coming in as I left for school.

177

But that had not happened for a long time.

I waited until they had almost reached the harbour and lifting my jacket, prodded my young brother. As usual, he was sprawled out on the settee.

"That's the boats comin' in Calman. Ye better get your shoes on if you're comin'."

There was no response. I pulled on my jacket then prodded him again, harder this time.

"Stop pretendin' you're asleep, get UP."

The brat was probably acting up, as usual. I was in no mood for his silly games, and leaning forward I whipped the cover off the huddled figure.

"I SAID. THAT'S THE BOATS. Now for the last time, are ye comin' or not?"

His eyes opened but he made no move to get up. Beneath the tangled shock of red hair, I noticed his face was unusually pale. With a sigh, I sat down on the edge of the settee. All he ever seemed to do nowadays was sleep.

"Whit's the matter wi' ye Calman? Why are ye not round playin' with Sandy and Iain? Ye seem to spend your time lyin' around here doin' nothing."

Expressionless, he watched me fastening my jacket. I shrugged.

"Well since ye don't seem to know what ye're doin', I'm away."

For several moments he lay staring into the fire then he said:

"I'm not feelin' well. I was sick again today."

The words were barely audible.

"But don't tell Faither. He doesn't believe me, thinks I'm jist dodgin' out of unloadin' the catch."

If there is a catch, I thought, things were becoming so bad, we'd be lucky if there was anything to unload. I stood up.

178

Calman had probably gorged himself with crisps and sweets, and was getting no sympathy from me.

"All right, but ye better tell Mammy ye've been sick again, and she'll tell ye the same I've been tellin' ye for weeks, ye better stop eatin' all that rubbish. Look at ye, you're as white as a sheet."

He turned away from me and closed his eyes.

It was almost dark by the time I reached the harbour and looking round the grim faces, I realised many had come back empty handed. There were about a dozen or so men, all local fishermen, and as I made my way along the pier, the talk was mainly about tonight's meeting. Local and regional councillors would be there along with respresentatives from the fishing industry to discuss the present crisis.

My father and Uncle Murdo were alongside the *Norseman* talking with several other men and I gathered from the conversation that Lachlan MacLeod had no intention of going to the meeting. He was standing apart from the others, his back towards them with his arms folded, glowering out to sea. I saw his brother Donald say something to my father then he walked over to Lachlan. A heated exchange followed.

The arm waving and shouting went on for several minutes, then thrusting his hands into his jacket pockets, Lachlan turned abruptly and strode off up the pier. As he drew level with my father's boat, he paused and jerked his thumb towards the village hall.

"I take it you're all goin' then?"

Some of the men nodded. Lachlan stared at them morosely then shook his head.

"A waste of time. Sittin' around there tellin' us it's got nothing to do with that damned reactor. They're probably told to say that. Bunch of lying bastards."

He spat viciously and glared round the circle of men.

"You all saw the leaflet they handed out after the last radiation leak: 'No immediate danger.' That's a laugh. Try tellin' that to all the dead fish. Or the bank manager, when ye can't keep up the payments on your boat."

He glared pointedly at his brother. Donald shifted uncomfortably and when he spoke, he avoided Lachlan's gaze.

"Well, everyone should come along at least, just to hear what they have to say. If they are goin' tae give us subsidies, it might be worth our while."

Lachlan spun round. For a moment I thought he was going to strike his brother. Instead, he threw back his head and laughed bitterly.

"Is that what they're callin' it, subsidies? Sounds more like bribery to me. Paying us to keep our mouths shut about what's happening here. Mind you, I suppose the money will come in handy to pay for funerals and the likes, and by Christ, there's been plenty of them."

Some of the men shook their heads but nobody said anything. Lachlan looked slowly round the familiar faces and when he spoke his voice was unusually quiet.

"You just don't get it, do you? High levels of radiation are lethal. And it's not just the accidents I'm talking about. What worries me is the tons of radioactive waste they're dumping into the sea."

For several moments, he stared out across the harbour then he shook his head, turned, and made his way up the pier.

And Lachlan had good reason to be worried. Married less than two years, his young wife Jean had recently lost her second child, miscarried in the fifth month. Now the hospital at Inverness had told them she might never be able to have children. And his father, a man who'd never had a day's

180

illness in his life, had just been told he had a tumour.

On the way back to the house, my father asked about Calman. I said he was probably away playing at Vikings. Later on, he was too preoccupied about the meeting to notice that Calman had not eaten any of his dinner.

Over the next few weeks, Calman's condition worsened and when his tests came back, he was told he would have to go into hospital. Doctor Morrison said they had no idea what it was at this stage, but, from his evasive manner, I received the impression he was not telling my father the full story.

And for the first time in my life, I was afraid. Through the long dark nights I would lie awake, the fear never left me and at times I'd be overwhelmed by black despair. I could not help thinking about Lachlan's nephew, Rory MacDonald, and there was no doubt in Lachlan's mind what had caused his death. But he could not prove it.

Last summer, Rory had taken ill. He'd been flown to the hospital in Glasgow where it was confirmed that he had leukaemia and two months later, on the day he would have been eight, he died.

His parents ran the farm up at the North croft, and they'd received another blow when the man from the Ministry of Agriculture had told them all their cattle had to be destroyed. Something about the milk not being up to standard but the results of the tests were never explained. The MacDonalds were not the only ones. After the accident at the reactor, several of the other farms had been cleared; some of the crofters had already left and others were talking about it.

My father never spoke about Calman. For hours on end he would stand out beside the back porch, staring out across the North sea and I noticed the strain in the tanned, weather-beaten face.

Calman had been away about eight weeks, and I was

helping my mother in the kitchen when we heard a car draw up. A few minutes later there was the sound of doors banging, and men shouting.

Then my father, supported by Lachlan and Donald, staggered into the hall. He was drunk. Dead drunk. I was shocked, my father never even took a dram at New Year. My mother burst into tears and Lachlan tried to get him to sit down. But he refused.

Shouting and roaring like a madman, he pushed Lachlan away and stumbled out into the back porch. Then we heard the sound of things crashing as he rummaged through the cupboard. There was no reasoning with him and we watched in silence, as he dragged a drum of petrol down towards the rowing boat he kept on the shore. He reached the boat and began throwing boulders and anything he could lay his hands on, in the general direction of the nuclear reactor.

His intention, as far as we could gather, was to row across the bay, set fire to the reactor, and blow it to kingdom come.

Donald had to physically restrain him and eventually managed to drag my father away from the boat. He collapsed on the shore and it was the first time I ever saw my father cry. He just sat there, rocking backwards and forward, repeating Calman's name over and over, weeping like a child.

Lachlan came over to where I was standing and gently laid his hand on my shoulder.

"Leave him be for a while. Donald and me will bring him up and put him into his bed."

He stared out across the bay then went on.

"Don't be too hard on him. Your father's a good man and tonight, everything came to a head. The anger, the bitterness, the cold fury seething within him finally erupted, and now in his anguish, he blames himself for what's happened to Calman."

He looked at me thoughtfully for a moment and when he

spoke, there was a flat finality in his tone.

"In today's society, money is all that matters. How people feel about a nuclear power station, an oil refinery or a toxic waste incinerator on their doorstep, is of no consequence. If they object, they're accused of standing in the way of progress, progress of course, being just another word for money, and they're branded as troublemakers."

He paused and I saw his jaw tighten as the anger stirred within him. At length he turned and seeing my puzzled frown, grinned.

"Ach, I shouldn't be talking like this, lass. Maybe it's not all gloom and doom. You see, there is one small consolation, if you can call it that."

"What's that?"

He picked up a pebble and hurled it into the sea.

"Think about it."

He set off towards my father and called over his shoulder.

"If things continue the way they're going, the fools will wipe themselves out along with the rest of us."

Small consolation indeed.

Every weekend, my parents would take the train down to Glasgow and when they returned, I could hear my mother sobbing in her room. I knew Calman was not getting any better. Then I heard Doctor Morrison talking to my parents about how people with leukaemia respond differently. Some lasted longer than others.

I had no idea what happened to a person with leukaemia. My mother had told me it was something to do with the blood, but the full horror of the evil, wasting disease did not register until, by chance, I overheard Rory MacDonald's sister, talking to one of the girls at school.

Fiona had been by his bedside when he died and her eyes reflected the horror which would remain with her for the rest of her life. She described the small, unconscious figure on the bed, helpless, gravely ill, and how she'd stood, transfixed, watching the blood pour from his mouth, his ears, his eyes. His body jack-knifed violently, and with one final bubbling scream of agony he pitched forward, and his young life slipped away.

Fiona said the bed looked like the scene of a massacre.

The following week I heard that Calman was coming home. By now I knew the doctors could do no more for him and they had told my father it would only be a matter of weeks.

I hardly recognized the emaciated, tiny figure. It was as if he had shrunk. And he had no hair, the treatment had left him bald. But he had good days, as well as bad ones. And on the good days I would prop him up, then I'd help him to put on his Viking helmet, half of a coconut shell, and wrap the old sheepskin rug round his shoulders, and as he clutched his wooden double-headed axe, I'd tell him stories. The more gruesome the better.

He confided however, that my stories were not as good as Grandpa Ragnar's. Heads had to be sliced off, the enemy hacked to pieces, villages ransacked, pillaged, and in Grandpa Ragnar's stories, nobody, not even the hens, were spared.

Grandpa Ragnar, in more ways than one, had a lot to answer for. To begin with, he'd refused to call Calman by his name, said it was a sissy name (Calman is the gaelic for dove) and he insisted on calling him Lars, the young Berserker.

Then, at the ripe old age of seventy-two, during one of his inordinate drinking bouts, he'd run off with the home help, a buxom girl in her late twenties. It was still the talk of the place.

But Calman worshipped him. He was of Viking descent, which probably explained his outrageous behaviour.

My mother made a bed up in the living room for Calman, and each night we took turns of sleeping on the settee. If the pain became unbearable, we'd been told to give him another of the pills Doctor Morrison had left. He never complained, even when it was obvious he was suffering. And he did not seem to fear death. He'd only spoken about it once. He knew he was going to Valhalla, for Grandpa Ragnar had told him, and because he was brave, he would be a berserker when he got there.

As the weeks passed, Calman grew weaker. Three days before Christmas, he'd had a particularly bad day and I offered to sleep in the living room to let my mother get some rest. Around three I wakened with a start. I could not hear Calman breathing. Within seconds I was over beside his bed, but he was not there.

My hand flew to my mouth in panic and grabbing my shawl, I stumbled towards the porch. As I fumbled with the latch, it suddenly occurred to me I was being hysterical. Calman could hardly sit up, far less go off wandering, into the night. My mother had probably taken him through to her room. For several minutes I stood listening for any sound, but everything was quiet. I turned and was about to go back through to the kitchen when a glimmer of light caught my eye through the porch window. Wiping the glass, I peered outside and in the pale light of the moon, I could see the faint, orange glow of a lantern, weaving backwards and forwards at the water's edge. Instinctively, my body stiffened.

Although I knew it could not possibly be Calman, somebody was down there. But who? And what were they doing there at this hour of the night?

For several minutes, I stood motionless, watching, listening, then pulling my shawl around my shoulders, I tentatively opened the porch door. The light from the almost full moon cast a strange, shimmering, silver glow over the familiar shoreline and as I picked my way over the rough shingle, I could feel my legs begin to tremble.

I'd gone about four, maybe five hundred metres when I stopped short. I couldn't be certain, but I thought I could hear singing. Tuneless, raucous singing, and laughter. Then I heard a splash and the singing ceased abruptly. Suddenly, I caught the outline of a figure, crouched at the water's edge. They appeared to be searching for something, then the person stood up and there was no mistaking Grandpa Ragnar's huge, burly frame.

As he turned, he caught sight of me. There was a fractional hesitation then lifting his arm, he waved. As he staggered towards me, I could see he was clearly the worse for drink.

Clutching a jug, his "wassail" as he called the dreadful concoction he secretly brewed, he reeled to a halt about an arm's length from where I was standing and attempted to focus. Then he lurched forward and put his arm round my shoulder, for support, more than anything else, and belched. Appalled by his disgraceful performance, I pushed him away. Had he no respect? I glared at the swaying figure.

"Do you know Calman is very ill?"

He continued to hum to himself then he half turned and said:

"Was . . . but not any more."

"What do you mean?"

By way of reply, he held the jug up towards the sky in a gesture of salutation, and offered the customary Norse greeting of good health to his pagan god, Odin.

"Ves Heill!"

Then he up-ended the jug, took a prolonged swig and belched again. Ignoring my icy stare, he wiped his lips and as he replaced the cork on the jug, said matter-of-factly:

186

"Young Lars is gone."

Incredulous, I spun round.

"He's what? What do you mean, he's gone? Gone where?"

It occurred to me at this point he'd actually taken leave of his senses then I followed his gaze. And in the shimmering light of the moon I saw the boat. At that moment, an orange pillar of flame streaked upwards from the stern, lighting up the sea. As the flames spread, the bow lifted and the small craft heeled fractionally, then she levelled and gathering speed, headed towards the open sea.

I stood transfixed, staring out over the dark, lifting swell. Through my tears, I watched the boat until it became a speck, then it disappeared, over the indigo horizon.

Calman had got his wish. He had gone to Valhalla, with a send-off befitting to a young Viking warrior. For it was only then I realised Grandpa Ragnar was in full Viking dress.

How long we stood there, I have no idea. But, abruptly, without a word, Grandpa Ragnar wheeled round, and staggered off into the night. As I watched the large figure disappear into the darkness I realised that I'd completely misjudged Grandpa Ragnar. He loved Calman, and true to his word, he'd honoured the promise he'd once made.

A feeling of devastating emptiness and longing swept through me, knowing I would never see my wee brother again, and brushing the tears from my cheeks, I turned and made my way slowly back towards the house.

As I reached the fence, I was surprised to see my father standing beside the gate. He did not speak. For a while, he stood gazing out across the sea. Then he stepped forward. Unconsciously almost, he nodded to himself in slow understanding, and clasped his big, calloused hand round mine.

Joe Thomson (7)

*Asthma Attack

Mum had asked me to fetch the iron.
I was in the garden
trying to reach the steps.

I felt like a ghost,
like I could put my hand
through my chest.

"Hurry up!" she shouted.
"I'm going out tonight.
I need my black blouse."

I tried to say something,
like, "Mum",
but wheezed instead.

Then I heard crunch, crunch
on the gravel,
and saw her feet.

"Joe,
what are you doing
down there?" she said.

Cathy Baker (12)

Earthbound

Jan looked out of her window: in front of her, ranged across the dark sky, and lit only by the crescent moon, stood the figures of legend: here was Orion the Hunter, and his prey Lepus the Hare or perhaps Taurus the Bull, or even possibly one of the bears, the Ursae Major or Minor, and the Hunter's two dogs pointing the way; there was the Queen Cassiopeia, and the King Cepheus, their daughter Andromeda (what great life might lie in the cloud behind her beauty!) and her rescuer Perseus from the great monster Cetus. All the stories the ancients had told were still alive in the sky, but now they were only names, concealing the great wonders that could serve today as legend: wonders of science instead of story.

She saw the individual stars: Polaris at the zenith, and red Betelgeuse, even redder Antares and blue Rigel, and bright, bright Sirius who lay almost at the horizon. Somehow, that star intrigued her most: it was common knowledge now that it had one companion, a white dwarf which affected the main star as if it were the planet to Sirius A's sun; many people nowadays even knew that once the tiny white dwarf had been the Sirius A; but what about the reports people had been hearing of a third star, a Sirius C?

It was hard to believe: you would think that the great telescopes on Earth and in the sky, and now the one that was being talked about, that would be carried on a space probe to the planet Mars, would by now have revealed any companion. But this discovery had come from the amateurs, such as Jan herself, fresh from university, and the radio telescopes that had picked up irregular beeps from the place where Sirius C might stand. Not the signals of a pulsar, or one of the many radio galaxies that had been found to litter the sky: signals changing in pace and even pitch, when they had experimentally been fed through a loudspeaker. The scientists would almost have said it was a language, if the sounds had not been so alien to their ears. They had even broadcast it on the radio for pure interest as a filler, so now all the world knew of the mystery of "Sirius C".

Jan took a small look through her telescope, aiming it roughly in the direction of bright Sirius: and as she did so she thought she had been blinded, for Sirius appeared to explode in a great flash of white light, and fill the whole sky. But when she rubbed her eyes, there was nothing: only the bright star on the edge of the sky.

Then something came round again, like a nova – no, supernova, for it was so bright – and Jan recognised the "lighthouse effect", light sweeping towards her and then away, so that it looked to be a flash. Immediately, Jan snatched up the telephone next to the window, to call the observatory.

But when she got through, they had seen nothing, and advised her that she was getting tired, she ought to be getting to bed.

Jan was puzzled – she *had* seen something. So excitedly she left her flat, and knocked on the door of the flat next door.

"Go away, you silly young thing!" said a grumpy Mrs Witherspoon. "I can't see anything out of my window, only stars, and not many of them, because of all this cloud."

Cloud? thought Jan, and returned home, and looked out of her window again. No cloud – in fact, the sky was perfect, with not an inch of cloud obscuring it.

"Maybe they're right," thought Jan. "It is late – I should really go to bed."

She did so; and surprisingly for her, she dropped straight off to sleep.

*

Jan awoke suddenly – she turned over sleepily, only to be informed by her alarm clock that it was one in the morning.

"Honestly!" she began to say – but then she noticed the sweeps of light again, across the sky.

"Meteor shower!" she said in recognition, turned her bedside lamp on, and opened up her almanac complete with the dates of the great showers. Nothing – she was a month after the Leonids, and nothing more to be expected for ages to come. A new shower? The Siriids? Possible – but unlikely.

Then she heard a voice. It was deep, deeper than could be expected from any earth language, and it spoke as if English came very unnaturally to it.

"Greetings, Earthling," it said in its deep tone.

"What?" Jan was still sleepy.

"You are the chosen one, Earthling. You of all your kindred have been chosen by us to lead the way forward; you have been chosen to show your kind what in truth lies beyond their Sun. They are restricted to this earth: but now you are not. Simply come with us and you will be as free as we are."

Jan jerked her head forward, out of sleep completely.

"What kind of joke is this?"

"What is a joke?" the voice said, and Jan could feel its emotionless monotone. "We are sincere, completely so. You are the herald of what can be a new age of understanding."

Jan the history scholar took over from Jan the astronomer. "A new Renaissance?"

"We do not know the word. But if you become our herald, your world could rise to our heights. Our heights and the heights of every other race now extant. We do not know why your world is so backward. Many times we have come, but in each case we have been repelled. We have come to many of your world, but we are never trusted, never accepted. You must come."

"And if I do not?"

"This must be our last visit, Earthling."

Jan did not ask why.

"If the offer is lost now, then your world will never advance further. You have done quite well – but you are the slowest, and the last, to progress. Every other world has taken us in. We cannot understand why yours will not also."

"What do have I have to lose?

"You have nothing to lose, Earthling – but you have everything to gain."

"If this is some kind of practical joke . . ." Jan said.

"We repeat, what is a joke? We have no concept of jokes."

"Where are you from?" Jan asked.

"Your tongue will not pronounce its name. We must resort to the name you know it by. Now you call it Sirius C."

Sirius C!

"I'll come," Jan said impulsively, although not knowing in her heart what she should do.

"We are sure that you made the right choice. Ascend with us."

Ascend?

"You will see before you a . . . a bridge, I believe you call it. Climb it and you will be in our heights. Then you will see the task ahead."

And a bridge there was: to Jan's eyes it was made up of millions upon millions of points of light, which she knew had to be stars. Her bedroom, meanwhile, had vanished; she stood alone on the bridge, surrounded by the night sky.

Jan stepped off the end of the bridge, and she appeared to be standing on – she screamed, because she saw nothing between her feet.

"There is no need to be afraid," a voice said kindly, in the same tones of the last voice Jan had heard, but now it spoke fluently. And then Jan knew that the voice was no longer

192

speaking English, but instead the language that had been heard in the broadcasts of the Sirian signals: she knew now that this was no joke, that this was completely sincere.

"You are with us now," the voice continued. "You need not traverse space in the same way your earthbound kinsmen do."

Jan could hear the voice grow ever further away from her: on an impulse, she followed it, to hear it grow nearer again.

"Now you will see the universe," the voice said, "now you will see what your comrades on your world cannot see, because they are too blind to look."

And Jan saw.

She saw the great stars, Betelgeuse and Rigel and Regulus and Antares, all shining in their various colours as if they were fairy lights to the black sky's tree.

She saw through the clouds of dark matter that obscure much of the universe: those clouds of dark matter that *are* much of the universe, and beyond them she saw constellations, galaxies, stars, worlds in ways none had ever seen them before, whole new places that she was the only one privileged enough to see.

She saw great collections of stars in fabulous shapes, and the nebulae of the universe that serve as maternity-wards for ever more young stars to be born, and all their different shapes, the Horsehead and Trifid and Andromeda and Orion.

She saw nova and supernova, the fireworks of the universe, and the setters-free of many of the great elements that went into the worlds as they were formed.

She saw galaxies in many forms, spiral and elliptical and irregular; and she saw into them, first the stars and then the worlds that orbit them; and there she saw towns, cities such as her own, with people that could be anyone she knew: but there was always a difference, and that was that they were so much more advanced than anything Jan knew.

She saw the mystic Zodiac, and stars like the Sun traversing it; she saw other worlds, other races looking at it in their different ways, and all of them knew that they were not alone.

She saw the variable stars, that serve as measurers for the universe to be guided by; and she saw the beauteous multiple stars, whole systems all orbiting around each other, in colours that none save her had ever seen.

She saw the quasars which all but she on her world thought to be the outer bounds of the universe: and then she saw beyond the quasars, seeing whole new worlds, and seeing them at every stage of time.

And from these great things she saw smaller things: molecules and atoms and even what lies inside them, the mysterious particles, hadrons and photons and tachyons and even stranger things that only she could truly fathom.

And she saw the enigmas of the universe, the black holes, which were again thought to be outer limits, through which none could pass; and she alone ventured near one, in one, and then through one, which none save she had ever considered possible; and when she left it, she found herself in a world almost identical to her own, a parallel universe to hers: and she journeyed through many of these holes, using them simply as bridges to cross space and time.

And she journeyed for eternity.

And then she found herself back in the place which was Sirius C: and she heard the voice speak to her again.

"I see that you are returned."

It was the first time she had heard any kind of singular pronoun from the voices. Sensing that something was about to change, she listened carefully.

"We are no longer an entity that must speak to you as one. You have made the Journey now. You are one of us."

"Who are you?" she asked, no longer the Earthling once known as Jan, but a cosmic being, a part of the universe itself.

"Our name is unpronounceable in your strange tongue. Your race has called us by many names. Some call our name creator, others call it god. Many among us also have names. I am supreme among us, because I was the first: I have been called Zeus or Jupiter, Ra or Wotan or Odin."

Now the second voice.

"And my name has been called Athena or Minerva, Freya or Friga, Ishtar or Hera, Venus or Aphrodite: my names are myriad."

A third voice, which so far the new creator, the youngest Herald of many, had not yet heard.

"My names are myriad also, but all among you know me. I have been known as Mars or Ares, Tiw or Tir, Thor or Horus, Hephaestus or Vulcan."

Now a fourth voice. Younger, but still old, extremely old.

"I was the first among the Heralds. This race of creators came to our planet first. They were first in the universe: they were born before our worlds, our suns had even started to be made. By the time they came to us, they were as one with the universe: they had no use for their physical bodies, being simply intelligence, and great intelligence, beyond anything we had known. With their help, my race was able to progress, until it spread across a whole galaxy.

"Your people have called me Hermes or Mercury, because I am a herald and a messenger, as you will be. Now you must be Herald to your people. Return to them, and you will teach them the way forward. Soon space will be in their hands."

She returned now, no longer a simple Earthling, but a Herald intended to show those who were once her people the way forward so that they could achieve their innate potential to venture into space, to harness the energies of the stars, to use that to travel. The people who had sent her, the people called creator or called god, hoped that soon their task would be over, until new races emerged: that all the creatures of the universe would be sufficiently advanced to fend for themselves, and to discover the mysteries of their wide home.

But in her heart of hearts she knew it would never happen: she knew the planet Earth would remain as it was now, a backwater of the universe, its people never daring to go beyond the atmosphere that tied them to the planet to which they were born. For they would never understand unless they saw: for them, seeing alone was believing. But they would never see unless they understood: for although everything was there, their eyes would not see them. It was a circle from which they would never escape. For while she was free to roam now about all that there would ever be, this freedom would never come to her people: for they were, and would always be, earthbound.

I AM THE SPIRIT OF
RAIN AND WIND

Benna Harper (16)

Vanessa Nicholson (12)

Just Another Winter Morning

I flung open
The pleated school skirts.
The gold brooch
Shone brightly
onto our unmown
Green cloak –
Covered in a sparkling
Madonna dress.
Perhaps next year
Angel gowns
Will fall.

A little
Santa suit
Hopped up to the
Glasses
I was looking out of.
I looked at our neighbour's
Green velvet, flaring ball dress
Hung up with
scrunchies.
We had taken ours down
ages ago . . .

A layer of fragile Lace collars
lay upon the Pond.

The weather had given up
Crystalling
And now it lightly
Grey buttoned.

The upside down
Choirboy gowns
Opened out their tiny white
Gloves
And let the
Grey buttons
Refresh them.

Just another Winter morning.

Mark Johnson (12)

The Storm

John sat up, his face moist with sweat. His head throbbed and he shivered with the sudden cold. Thoughts span round his mind, visions and illusions. There was a second of confusion, then he relaxed onto the comfortable bed.

It was a cold, damp night. "Not the night to wake up in," thought John, taking stock of his surroundings. The wind groaned and whistled around the big old house, searching for a way in. Harsh drops of rain, sprinkled heavily on the creaking roof, trickled and flowed over the broken tiles, only to be collected in the fast-moving gutters. Angry rumbles of thunder bellowed in the raging night sky, and the hemisphere was alight with vicious bolts of lightning, poking at the ground with long fingers.

John sighed. He hated sleepless nights, more so in this house. His parents had purchased it recently, at a surprisingly low price. It was huge, and quite old so it needed a lot of work, but his Mum and Dad were happy. The kitchen was large, making cooking easier, and the study on the top floor delighted his Dad, who was constantly at work. But nothing seemed right to John. As far as he could see, there was nothing good about the house, no real bonus to him. In fact he Hated it. And a night like this just showed the reasons why.

Eerie creaks filled the house. It seemed doors were constantly opening, with hinges that creaked and screeched like an angry vulture. The floorboards were loose and jutted out at angles all over the polished wooden floor. In high winds it even felt like the house was swaying, and the moans and groans of the rotting timber just added to the total feeling of

Sarah Knight (13)

despair. But what he thought was the worst of all was the darkness. There were always corners and alcoves that were kept in constant darkness. The design of the building ensured that weird shadows were thrown across the walls, giving a mysterious air to the place. It had been a good game when they first moved in, to search the little cupboards and corners of the place. But now it didn't seem like a game. It just felt unsettling, and maybe even fearsome.

His thoughts were broken by a brilliant explosion of bright light that lit up his room and brought him to his senses.

John lay back, his heart pounding, and began to count. One, tw— a disconcerting grumbling rang out from the heavens, a clap of thunder. The storm was only a few miles away, and it was getting closer. The prospect filled him with fear, and he lay, cowering on the bed, terror creeping into his mind. Where were his parents? Trembling, he stretched out his hand, and fiddled with his bedside lamp, on a flaking white table by his head. His shaking hands had trouble getting to the switch, but John closed his eyes and pressed the small white button. The room was illuminated by a dim light faintly outlining the cracked and crumbled plaster. The small glow at first seemed friendly, and John felt relieved and safe, but as he looked out into the dusty bedroom he felt altogether different. In fact, the place seemed just as eerie as before, and threatening shadows were cast by little objects on the dark walls. The fear crept back at John as the shadows seemed to grow bigger and bigger, surrounding him in a battlement of darkness. The blackness descended on him, closing in, enveloping him in a pocket of damp. A bolt of lightning struck through the air, clawing at the dirty, pale window, leaving John helpless in the corner. Another noise pierced the storm, the quiet humming of the little bulb, struggling against the shade. It flickered and died, plunging the room into pitch blackness. John froze, a chill passed through his body. For not the first time in his life, he felt alone, and very, very afraid. He desperately looked around, his eyes flitting from one place to another, unable to focus in the silken blackness of night. A strange cold feeling smothered his mind, and it seemed things were moving, stealthily, quietly, under the cover of the clouds. He felt helpless, and he was transfixed in a single spot, unable to move. The storm grew, ever gathering speed, and closing upon the house, tiny, compared to the great size of the buffeting elements. A forked tongue snaked down to the ground, colouring the sky in unnatural shades. A furious roar rocked the ground, shaking the building, while John lay terrified in his little room.

202

Iona Firoucabadi (15)

The rain poured down with added strength, intent on penetrating the old bricks. The darkness kept falling on John, damp and angry draughts bore down on him as he lay there, a weird sense of horror in his mind. The clouds rolled thunderously overhead, drumming out frightening claps, and the wind blew with all its strength, bending the trees mercilessly like a ship at sea.

It grew bigger and bigger, louder and louder. John cried out in vain, throwing the bedclothes over his head, to protect himself from the invisible enemy. The unseen danger gained power, speeding across the skies, the sound turning fever pitch. It rang around John's ears, bursting his eardrums, until he was sure he could take it no longer. The building moaned and grumbled under the weight of the elements, creaking unnaturally in a fit of trouble. The sky darkened and gave out a scream that filled the room, bouncing off the walls, vibrating his whole being. The house wailed like a banshee, the wind grew stronger, and John heard a huge fearsome bellow that left him shivering, terrified. In despair, he tried to count the seconds between lightning and thunder. He spoke aloud, his voice wavering. One. He willed the storm to stop. Two, three, four. Where was the screaming clap he was waiting for? But when it did come, it was quieter, and further away. Then realization hit John. The storm was moving off! A weight was lifted from his shoulders, and for the first time this evening, he smiled. He waited, pondering what to do, dazed and confused. As he sat up his eyes made out the familiar shapes of his belongings. A calmness returned to the little neighbourhood and he relaxed, his body tired. What had once been fierce and terrifying, now didn't seem so strange. He felt silly but relieved, glad that it all seemed over. The room was still dark, but John didn't care. He was just glad that he could go back to sleep. A warm feeling passed over him, of joy and happiness, and he slumped back cheerful, but ashamed of being so stupid. The sense of happiness was overwhelming. He closed his eyes and lay back, a smile on his face, into deep fitful slumber.

Then the blackness of the room was broken by a ray of golden light, coming from the door. The warm light spread across the room, spilling over John's face.

A head peeked through the door, and a familiar voice rang in his ears.

"I hope you weren't worried by the storm. I've just come up to check."

John opened his eyes, slowly turning his head.

"No Dad," said John confidently. "I hardly noticed it."

Christopher Heaney (12)

Tara Brett (8)

*The Storm

The time of day is noon.
I rage through the rain and the wind –
I stop, the rain stops.
The wind is still.
I gallop off.
I am the spirit of rain and wind,
I bury my foot prints in the ground.
Can I see what god is thinking?
The rain starts again . . .
Now I know what god is thinking –
He is thinking about a human being,
Caught, in the storm.

Lisa Woolnough (8)

Midnight Noises

I live by the swaying sea,
Each night I hear sounds that sometimes
make me shiver and sometimes sounds that
seem to rock me to sleep,
The crashing of the waves against the rocks,
The shuffling of the ghost people moving
nimbly across the sand,
The whispering of the trees in our back yard,
I don't know what happens by the oozy sea
at night.

Adam Smith (9)

THERE WAS ONCE A RABBIT

Elizabeth Willens (17)

Herbie

I pushed some sunflower seeds through the silver bars of his cage. His tiny paws clutched them tightly before shoving them into his already bulging cheek pouches. At last his cheeks had just too much, so he battled his way through the ribbons of Andrex tissue paper and the bundles of hamster bedding, to deposit the food in his rapidly growing pile of food. He emerged from the debris only to sniff about hungrily for more seeds! When he realised there was none, he turned, padded back to his house and slipped in.

Hours later, well into the night, a twitching pink nose pressed its way out, followed by two black beady eyes and finally, Herbie himself. He paused, as if looking for danger, with his nose quivering and his eyes watching. When he was sure he was safe, he ambled over to his drinking bottle and eagerly gulped down the cool, refreshing water. He went to the toilet and then clambered up his ladder to the second floor.

This top floor was a hamster multi-gym which included an exercise wheel, a fun-filled tube and gnawing log. Herbie waddled with his whiskers quivering, over to the log, pushed it out of the way, sat down and began to wash himself. He licked his paws and smoothed them over his head, scratching in every nook and cranny. His golden coat shone like new at the end and his ears were now fully up and alert. After scuttling through his tube he climbed on to his exercise wheel. He gnawed on the wood and amused himself until dawn came.

The next night he shook at the cage door, yearning to be let out. I opened it and he climbed into his roly-ball. He sailed about in that for a while, and when I put him back in he was exhausted. But a few snoozes later he was up and running about on his wheel and tube. I left him there noisily entertaining himself.

Twelve months have passed. I push some sunflower seeds into his cage. I stand back waiting for his pink button nose to appear. It doesn't. I rattle the cage bars. Still no movement. An uneasy feeling creeps over me. I gently remove the lid of his nesting box and dig down through the shredded bedding. My fingers sense the unusual temperature and I lift him up. His form is unyielding and cold to my touch. Where was his nuzzling nose, or his twitching whiskers? His warmth had been taken from him and his body was hard and rigid. His tiny paws were clasped around his face and his eyes were screwed up. He was dead.

Herbie was buried on 29th October 1994 under the sycamore tree.

Rest In Peace

James Donaghey (8)

Pig Murder

A man with a knife,
Sharpened by stone,
Comes to kill a pig.
Squeals come from the pig,
The man makes three slits in the pig's throat.
He sticks the knife between the lungs,
And pulls the knife down slowly,
Leaving a trail of blood,
Thick and red.
The man picks up the pig,
Sticks it upside down on stake in tree.
The pig's heart rolls out and falls to the ground,
Blood drips from the pig's mouth,
Making a puddle of blood.

Benjamin Arnold (11)

*The Friend

1   There was once a rabbit,
     A great, black rabbit,
     A long-eared, big-eyed rabbit,
     A short-haired, buck-toothed rabbit,

2   He ate like a traditional rabbit,
     A carrot and cabbage-diet rabbit,
     A water-in-the-bowl rabbit,
     A well-fed, well-bred rabbit,

3   This was a pioneering rabbit,
     A scared-of-nothing rabbit,
     A take-on-anything rabbit,
     A brave-as-a-bear rabbit,

4   But then there was a missing rabbit,
     A stolen-from-his-home rabbit,
     A searched-for, grieved-for rabbit,
     A never-to-be-forgotten rabbit.

Emma Lyall (15)

Ajay Chhabra (13)

His Beauty

Rippled in serried waves
Of yellow-framed, regal indigo
Against the peacock-green flushes
Of his designer-flapped wings.
"Sparky", we christened our pet budgerigar:
Flying by day and resting by night
In a confined domain
Which
Only he
Rules.
I hold his warm, tender lint body:
Wrapped in his coat of Robin Hood velvet,
Only broken by a golden crest beneath his beak.
I sense his microchip heart feebly throbbing
Against my climbing frame hand.
I gaze in awe at this wide-eyed creation
Of He, who produces only blueprints of freedom.
As he offers his beetle-shell claws,
I permit him to take me to be his lawful, fingered perch.
A white jet of treacle consistency
Now lies on my once clean finger:
Introducing into the room an acrid stench –
Normally unknown –
Disgracing his scentless reputation.
He opens his pistachio beak
In utterance of high-pitched jargon
Or a gracious apology.
Returning to his wonderland,
He nibbles upon a vine-shaped stick

Of his favourite millet grain
And washes down his lavish snack
With none but the best tapwater
From the cascading falls.
Having digested the food,
Through endless thrills
Of fluttering and swinging
On the flying trapeze,
He settles for some lower quality water
From the birdbath.
In a vain effort to clean his feathers,
I trigger a stream of water at him
Through an old air-freshener bottle.
Taken aback by my wanton cruelty,
He protests,
Fluttering inside his cage at breakneck speed –
Querulous and vindictive.
To compensate for my sins,
I release him –
Free –
To the kitchen and living room.
Chirping with delight
At one of his most relished pleasures,
He flits away.
A handful of marvels,
I observe,
Relating to the familiar phrase:
The best things in life are free!

Annie McDermott (8)

Annie McDermott (8)

Donkey's Story

I am a holy beast, I have been, ever since I carried Mary to the stable, the brightest stable in the world. You want to hear the story, do you? Alright. I'll tell it. It all began in Nazareth . . .

I came into it when we (i.e. me, Mary and Joseph) had to go to Bethlehem. I don't understand these taxes but it had to do with human ways. I walked for miles on stony roads, but even with Mary's coaxing and Joseph's manly, reassuring pats, I couldn't go much further. My hooves ached, and my hocks hurt, all my body felt stiff from the journey. It wasn't over yet though. Mary was heavier than I've known her to be before. Within my stomach, a pang of hunger broke out and wriggled around there. Without my noticing it, I was at a steady trot. I am a lively donkey and react naturally to leg signals, you see. There was a saying my grandpa told me, "every little bit helps". I was taking tiny steps now, but, for Mary's sake, I kept the trot steady.

She was heavy as a big beast with floppy ears and an ... err ... err ... ummmm ... Ahah! A trunk! Now I was walking again, then, I suddenly shied at a rabbit, then wouldn't move. Donkeys can be very stubborn when they want to, and I was being as stubborn as I could, now.

An inn loomed ahead, a few miles away, and we found that we were on the borders of Bethlehem. The inn was disappointing, for a clean-shaven Irish man (the innkeeper) said "Oh, aye, me inn's all crowded" and shooed us off when we knocked. At the next inn, out came a hollow sound, when we knocked. From the paddock, came a lowing, actually from a barn, and a soft snuffling came from the far field, only I could have noticed that. There was no room but we could sleep in the stable, as there was nowhere else, we accepted.

In that stable, and what a stable too, the animals were very contented. An ass, grey, hadn't an ounce of vice in her. She had a white muzzle, and snow-white socks. It was love at first sight, for her and me! She pawed the ground patiently to see how I would react. I bickered.

She had a disposition as sweet as sugar and Mary loved her too, I noticed (not as much as me!), as she patted her silken, sleek neck. Some ass, I thought.

Joseph, on the other hand, was busy with the ox telling him his life-story, he can be nutty sometimes! and the ox butted him playfully. He was boisterous, but tender hearted. He had horns as smooth as glass, and he was charging at the ass. I took my chance to be a hero, but no, he was playing.

That night I was so happy, as I curled up, for who curled

up next to me? The ASS! I snorted with contentment. Mary heard and patted me. Hours later I awoke, to find the stable totally transformed. It was lit up and there was a lot more than two humans. Also in the manger that I *would* be having my breakfast from lay a tiny human.

A bright circle was round his head. I found out his name was Jesus. Three well dressed men came, with grand gifts, camels followed obediently behind. Then men wearing tatty clothes, with lambs in their arms walked through the door. The Irish man came with his hands on his hips, wishing that the commotion was at his inn, but his face softened to a smile when he caught sight of what the ass beheld, I looked too, and our eyes met, true love, I thought, though the next thing that crossed my mind was "Father!" The ass had a foal, and it was healthy, and up, and nursing!

The next thing I knew was that the lambs had escaped and were gambolling with Willow (the foal) in the paddock. Then the ass and I were getting married, it was a simple sort of wedding, with Willow, the foal, as the page (he was a jack donkey) and the lambs as bridesmaids.

The visitors were the audience, and Mary and Joseph threw confetti. I loved every minute! All that mattered was we were married, and we were happy. When we got back to Nazareth Jesus was lying on my back, and the cross is there to prove it. I have never forgotten Mary's bouncy pat and Joseph's (again!) manly pat on my rump. You see, as Jesus was on my back he did the most important thing – patted me lightly, I always remember Jesus's pat. You now know why I am holy, all right, and you now know it wasn't just Jesus born on Christmas day, but Willow, too.

Poppy Corbett (8)

*Hilarious Hermit Crab

Gnarled like an old man's shaking hand.
Rough like the bark on an ancient apple tree.
Shaped like a falling fir cone.
Trapped in an aquarium.
A damp rocky desert marooned in moss.
Cinnamon ridges and fossilised sides.
Orange tipped feelers finding their way out.
Rich red claws timidly test the air.
Huge purple claw emerging.
Excited eyes slowly search about.
Six jointed legs support a house.
Scurrying smoothly across a bed of sand
the scavenger takes his feast.
A tasty finger or a morsel of food.
The Hermit Crab is satisfied
with the day.

Rachel Jamieson (5)

Ronan McKenna (10)

A Journey for the Vet

One dark dreary October night I had to stay in my Granda's country house, because he had a cow calving, and he did not want to be alone so my mum left me out. We went out at about half six in the evening to the byre. It was dark and wet and cold when we went out to check on her. Granda thought she was jumping an awful lot.

"Go and ring the vet," said Granda worriedly. So I ran to the house only to find the phone out of order. I hastily ran back to the byre and told Granda the bad news, he looked shocked. He ran over just to make sure. "I'll go and fetch the vet," he said worriedly. "No you stay with the calf, I'll get the vet," I replied. In some ways I was glad to get away but in others I wasn't. I was glad to get away from the smell of dung and hay and slurry, but I didn't want to leave my Granda on his own.

So without any disagreement I was quickly on my old bike and along the narrow country lane that goes past Granda's house. Although I wasn't looking forward to this risky journey I had to keep going. All I could see in front of me was complete darkness and the tall bare trees. After what seemed to be a very long time I eventually reached the vet's house, dropped the bike just beside the front door and banged at the door. Breathlessly I told the vet all about the situation. He put his hands on my shoulders and said "Try to calm down". He fetched his black bag of instruments and told me to get into the car. I hopped into the car, we drove towards the farm.

When we got to the cow at last the vet said, "She must be ready to calve now if she has been jumping that long." I couldn't bear to look because the vet said there might be blood. After a lot of coaxing and hard work he was born. The vet said he was a nice bullock. The cow was exhausted and so was I. The vet took the calf away outside and cleaned it up with old cloths.

I got to partly rear the calf. Granda lets me feed it whenever I go down to visit three times a week. I haven't sold the calf and never will because Granda says he would have died without my help.

Gemma Kegge (11)

The Snail

Two miniature horns extend from his head.
Two eyes on stems peruse the air.
A creamy yellow shell swirls on his back,
Protecting the body with no bones.
He travels his self-made silver path,
Meandering leisurely up a stem
Till he encounters a juicy leaf.
I see his dignity and grace;
Others abhor him and avert their sight.

Andrew McGarrigle (8)

*Pot Belly

Pot belly, pot belly pig
Ugly, shuffling, disgusting pig.
Snorting, grunting, thinking
Of old swill.
Lumbering, clumsily along
The ground
Appearances are ugly with his
Muggy look.

Pot belly, pot belly pig
Squelch!
Thinking piggy lonely in his sty
With just a scrap of swill,
But life's not like that,
In his mind he is a king.
Pot belly grunt!
With piles of swill and good mates
All a pig could want,
Pot belly pot belly pig.

Christopher Stopher (13)

The Walrus

The leviathan of the sea,
As you parade proudly.
But you are a crossbreed,
With your slug's body
And vampire's head.
Your blubber hangs in layers,
Like deflated balloons
And your whiskers are thick brown bristles
Entwined and matted,
Like thatch.
Your long teeth are greedy,
Like poker player's arms,
As you rake in the shellfish.

Vincent Whitfield (12)

226

Weaving the tides,
You emerge, take a deep breath,
And dive down.
Then you clamber onto the shore
And with your muscle fins
You are a drunk,
Clambering into bed.
People say you are dumb.
But really, in your head,
Ticks a time bomb,
Picking its moment to explode
And amaze us with your knowledge
Of the prehistoric depths of the sea's heart
Which you hold under your sodden hat
Until the world ends.

Polly Myatt (12)

HEAVY LABOUR IN THE WRITERS' BLOCK OF THE LOCAL POETENTIARY

Catherine MacDonald (17)

Chloë Coulson (10)

Sophie Robinson (11)

*The Waiting Wolf

First I saw her tiny feet
pointed and slim
sticking out under her
dainty red coat.
I gave her my heart,
flowers and all,
trying to stalk her.
That's the only way I know.
I felt sick
when she told me
about her Grandmother.
She bent over me.

As she did so
the jams in her basket
were spilling
all over the grass.
As I waited in Granny's bed
ruffled in nightgown, cap
and corset
I slid under the duvet
warm as an oven.
When she crawls in here
will she kiss my watering lips?
Will she smell my bad breath
as I breathe?
Will she feel my polished nose
on her chest
as she cuddles me?
As she comes into the room
my heart pounds.
Then I open my mouth wide.
She sees my teeth and tries to run,
but I corner her
and swallow her quickly.
Granny still repeats on me.
Granny tasted stale and rotten,
but Red Riding Hood
tasted like roast beef.
I hear scuffling in the room
but cannot see the door
my stomach is too big.
I feel like a pregnant woman
about to give birth.
Then split!
My stomach feels empty.

I see Red Riding Hood
and Granny.
Where did they come from?
My fur turns
from brown to red.
I feel pain all over.
Blood gushes like a waterfall
that falls from a high, steep cliff.

Glen Wallace (12)

Steven Barnett (7)

My Dragon

My pet dragon lived in my pencil pot.
She was as small as a tennis ball.
She threw my pencils out.
When I told my friends,
they said I was a liar.
I said, "Only because
you haven't got one!"
My mum thought my dragon
was my teddy Gizmo.
When my dragon got bigger,
her eyes were pieces
of melted red glass.
She cooked my dinner
with her breath. I shared
my egg and chips with her.
She drank acid bombs.

My dragon is dead now.
I buried her in the garden
under the shed with Gizmo.

233

Portia Barton (8)

*The Animal Parade

While we drove home
this winter's eve
I looked at the bare fields.

There on the horizon
I saw a line of trees and bushes
silhouetted against the grey and lilac sky.
As I looked
the trees seemed to move.

Some had the shape of bears
huge and shaggy
One resembled an elephant
lumbering along
behind a giraffe with a preposterous head.

I put my face
to the cool window
and wiped away the condensation.
Saw a tiger prowl
And seemed to hear it roar.

I turned to mum
"I saw some wild beasts"
She turns to look.
The beasts freeze
"Very nice dear"
She turns away.

234

The animals move on
marching through the night
guided by the eyes of a panther
Standing sentinel
and the flickering lights
of luminous insects.

As we neared the town
I saw an ungainly crocodile
approaching a massive flamingo
with a baby flamingo on its back.

But once we entered
the bright and bustling mass of roads
the animals were no more
Yet from my bedroom window
I will watch for them
and keep the secret
of the animal parade.

Hannah Cork (17)

Toby Collins (7)

In My Head

In my head there is a burglar alarm;
it rings when a fear tries to break in.
In my head there is a micro-chip
trying to buzz ideas.
In my head there is an egg;
it breaks up ideas
when I think of bad ones.
In my head there is a worm
telling me what to read
and what not to read.
In my head there is an ambulance
that smooths my pains away.
In my head there is a bulb
that lights up when
I have a great idea.

Nisha Doshi (8)

Electric Full Stops!

Nose pressed flat
Against the window,
All the way
From London to York;
I sat, rocked
By the rhythm of the track,
And teased
By the tilted, toothless grin
Of the cheeky Moon, on its back.
A train flashed past,
Like a blurred arrow of light,
Weaving through the cold January night;
Weaving through the miles of blackness,
Punctuated only
By amber dots,
Hovering,
Like a million electric full stops.

Nisha Doshi (8)

237

Katie Brown (15)

*London Lines

I'm taking the underground, to get around, because I
    haven't got a motor yet.
But I don't mind, I think, as I sit in my seat, all neat, and
    travel like a bubble up a drinking straw.
I head for the door, as more and more people get on.
I stick my card in the slot and I like it a lot when the
    machine sucks it in, right out of my hand,
Then I stand and wait for it to come out again. I see a
    poster on the wall advertising a do,
That would appeal to
The honest nine-to-fivers who would go with their friends
    from work, where they work as clerks
But what worries them is the traffic they'll have to fight
Coming home at night.
The sky has its urban turban on so I go into the local
As a man wearing bifocals comes out, then some louts,
    come out too.
They smell of booze, and the loos at Waterloo.
Inside the pub a mate offers to buy me a drink, and as I
    look at his pink face I know he owes me money.
But I'm not a bitter man so I order a lager instead.
My friend lights up and then frowns at the thugs
Taking drugs in the corner.
Soon I leave and go down to the dog track where I lean
    my back on the rail.
That place can be lonely, not only, if you've lost all your
    money, but at other times too.
It's late and I go and wait for the tube with the people in
    polyester

Who waited yesterday and the day before.
It's dark now and my Mum will be getting worried
About soap characters, who lead lives more exciting than
    hers, and Dad's slurs at Spurs matches
The last thing I notice is the loose-lipped indie youth culture
    being loose-lipped in my street
Before I go home to eat.

Lynn Walsh (8)

Doors

Big iron door
Green peeling paint
Flaking and showing grey metal
Empty barn full of rats.

Golden door
Seeks a house
The oak wood was
From a church

The pen door
Wire vining and weaving
Traps the animals
Inside.

The door with the padlock
Rusty, big and heavy
On the old shed
Where the motorbike rests.

French doors
Clitter and clatter when they close.
They see through
The dark hallway.

The cracked door
Cobwebs hanging
From top to bottom
Never opened.

Greenhouse door
Keeps the heat inside
The body
Warming the plants.

Slimy green door
Spikey top
Golden yellow tree
Alone.

Door of sand
Desert with no water
Camel quivers
In the heat haze.

Swan doors
Black with soot
Trap the fiery flames
Safe in the grate.

Lucinda Barrett-Nobbs (12)

Arched glass door
Golden handle
Into the secret garden.
My sister runs past.

Cat flap
Flapping
Wet fur
Puss jumps through.

Benjamin Marshall (8)

*My House

On one side of the door is a front hall.
On the other side is the great outdoors.
Far from the door is another door, just ignoring the first.
In front of the door is a driveway that looks one million
   miles long.
Upon the door is a woodworm, trying to nibble a hole.

Under the floor is earth, deeper than a sky scraper.
Opposite the floor is the ceiling as hard as rock.
Between the floor are people, wearing out the floor.

Within the storm are buckets of rain, wet as can be.
Next to the storm is the sun, trying to push its way in.
Beneath the storm are the helpless people, waiting for it to
   stop.

In front of the window is the howling wind.
On the window there is dirt, waiting to be washed off.
Over the window are spiders and ants wriggling around.

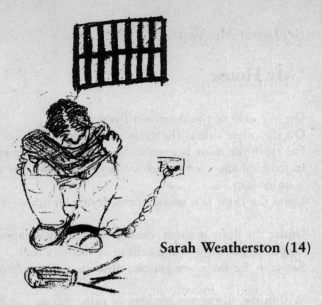

Sarah Weatherston (14)

Sarah Stringer (16)

**Poetic Justice

. . . you have been found guilty
by this court of
word murder.
I hereby sentence you to
six months'
heavy labour in the
writers' block of the local
poetentiary;
I also see fit to confiscate your
Poet's Licence for two years,
and I fine you the sum of
one thousand nouns.

Competitions

You write something.
Anything,
Something about dragons,
Or demons.
Then you send it off,
And start to wonder, "well,
Maybe the judges will prefer something about real life,
Or animals,
Instead of goblins."
And you think some more,
And become almost positive,
After reading the book of winners last year,
That they would prefer something about real life,
And animals,
And you wish your hardest that maybe they'd like yours,
But your body says "No,
No win."
Then you look at the book again,
And think,
"Well, mine was certainly better than that one,
And that one."
So you are refilled with hope,
And every day after that,
You're at the post,
Waiting for the letter.
Mine never came,
All you hopers out there.

SCHOOL PRIZE WINNERS

Three schools were awarded a School Special Award of £300 for submitting work of outstanding quality:

Dalriada School, Ballymoney, Co. Antrim, Northern Ireland
Halesworth Middle School, Halesworth, Suffolk
Tregelles the Mount School, York

The following schools won School Awards of £150 for submitting work of the most consistent merit:

Abbey County Infants' School, Darlington, Co. Durham
Abingdon School, Abingdon, Oxon
Bedgebury Lower School, Lillesden, Hawkhurst, Kent
Bishop Luffa School, Chichester, West Sussex
Blackheath High School, Blackheath, London
Budehaven Community School, Bude, Cornwall
Burnham Grammar School, Burnham, Bucks
Channing School, Highgate, London
Charters School, Sunningdale, Ascot
Foston CE School, Foston, York
Guildford High School for Girls, Guildford, Surrey
Handford Hall County Primary School, Ipswich, Suffolk
Hazel Grove High School, Hazel Grove, Stockport
Hebden Royd CE JMI School, Hebden Bridge, West
  Yorkshire
Hoe Bridge School, Woking, Surrey
James Allen's Girls' School, East Dulwich Grove, London
  SE22
Junior Kings School, Sturry, Canterbury, Kent
Marden High School, Cullercoats, Tyne and Wear
Meadow Green Primary School, Wythall, Birmingham
Newcastle under Lyme School, Newcastle under Lyme,
  Staffs

Notting Hill and Ealing High School, Ealing, London
Port Regis School, Shaftesbury, Dorset
Putney High School, Putney, London SW15
Roath Park Primary School, Cardiff
Royal Grammar School, Newcastle upon Tyne
The Park School, Dartington, Totnes, Devon
University College School Junior Branch, London NW3

INDEX